P9-EDT-972

PANORAMA

TO KNOW TO UNDERSTAND TO PARTICIPATE
THE CANADIAN HERITAGE IS YOUR HERITAGE

A Project of Alberta Education
Funded
By
The Alberta Heritage Savings Trust Fund
and
Dedicated to the Students
of Alberta
by the
Government of Alberta
1979

Grateful acknowledgment is extended
to those who assisted in the development
of the Alberta Heritage anthologies

Members of the Selection Committee

Theresa Ford / *Edmonton Catholic School District*
Michael Allen / *Calgary Catholic School District*
Tom Gee / *Alberta Education*
Marg Iveson / *Edmonton Public School District*
Gloria Limin / *Calgary Public School District*
Lorne MacRae / *Calgary Public School District*
Maureen Ross / *Edmonton Catholic School District*

Western Canadian Literature
for Youth

Theresa M. Ford
Managing Editor

Alberta Education
Edmonton

Alberta Education
Devonian Building
11160 Jasper Avenue
Edmonton, Alberta
T5K 0L2

ISBN 0-920794-18-1

Project Director/Dr. Kenneth Nixon
Design/David Shaw & Associates Ltd.
Publishing Consultants/Hurtig Publishers, Edmonton
Illustration/James McLachlan
Typesetting & Printing/Lawson Graphics Western Ltd., Calgary
Binding/Economy Bookbinding Company Ltd., Calgary

To the Reader

This anthology, *Panorama,* celebrates the beauty and magnificence of the land, the mountains, the sea and the sky of Western Canada.

While most Westerners delight in the variety of scenic tableaux available to them, individuals are particularly loyal to their favourite view. Some treasure "seeing the sky at eye level" on the vast plains, while others love the towering protection of the mountains. Still others are most at home gazing at the spectacle of the Pacific seascape, while those who have lived in the North find a particular splendour in the tundra or barren lands. Beauty is, indeed "in the eye of the beholder"!

The selections in this book not only describe the *Panorama* of the West but recount how people have coped with it. The great outdoors of Western Canada has given its people suffering and joy, poverty and riches, toil and relaxation. Always remember: it is *your* heritage. Love and preserve it!

Contents

Weather-wise

Landscape

WEATHER-WISE

The Promise

Bob Mason

Across the dim forbidding land
Like monuments of crystal sand
The wind has carved with practised hand
    A masterpiece of snow.
With every hue and line correct
To win the work the grim effect
    Of thirty-nine below!

A coyote wails the fading night
The pole-top owl is still and white
The rabbit crouches down from sight
    Of February's moon.
The drifts are like a frozen sea
Across a land that seems to be
    A thousand years from June.

The farmer forks his morning hay
By lantern light . . . frost bearded, grey
Saskatchewan is breaking day
    And how the wires sing!
Yet even in the level gleam
Of rising sun is lost the dream
    It ever can be spring.

The Wind Our Enemy

Anne Marriott

I

WIND
flattening its gaunt furious self against
the naked siding, knifing in the wounds
of time, pausing to tear aside the last
old scab of paint.

Wind
surging down the cocoa-coloured seams
of summer-fallow, darting in about
white hoofs and brown, snatching the sweaty cap
shielding red eyes.

Wind
filling the dry mouth with bitter dust
whipping the shoulders worry-bowed too soon,
soiling the water pail, and in grim prophecy
graying the hair.

II

The wheat in spring was like a giant's bolt of silk
Unrolled over the earth.
When the wind sprang
It rippled as if a great broad snake
Moved under the green sheet
Seeking its outward way to light.
In autumn it was an ocean of flecked gold
Sweet as a biscuit, breaking in crisp waves
That never shattered, never blurred in foam.
That was the last good year . . .

III

The wheat was embroidering
All the spring morning,

Frail threads needled by sunshine like thin gold.
A man's heart could love his land,
Smoothly self-yielding,
Its broad spread promising all his granaries might
hold.
A woman's eyes could kiss the soil
From her kitchen window,
Turning its black depths to unchipped cups — a silk
crepe dress —
(Two-ninety-eight, Sale Catalogue)
Pray sun's touch be gentleness,
Not a hot hand scorching flesh it would caress.
But sky like a new tin pan
Hot from the oven
Seemed soldered to the earth by horizons of glare . . .

The third day he left the fields . . .

Heavy scraping footsteps
Spoke before his words, "Crops dried out —
everywhere —"

IV

They said, "Sure, it'll rain next year!"
When that was dry, "Well, next year anyway."
Then, "Next —"
But still the metal hardness of the sky
Softened only in mockery.
When lightning slashed and twanged
And thunder made the hot head surge with pain
Never a drop fell;
Always hard yellow sun conquered the storm.
So the soon sickly-familiar saying grew,
(Watching the futile clouds sneak down the north)
"Just empties goin' back!"
(Cold laughter bending parched lips in a smile
Bleak eyes denied.)

V

Horses were strong so strong men might love them,
Sides groomed to copper burning the sun,
Wind tangling wild manes, dust circling wild hoofs,
Turn the colts loose! Watch the two-year-olds run!
Then heart thrilled fast and the veins filled with glory
The feel of hard leather a fortune more sweet
Than a girl's silky lips. He was one with the thunder,
The flying, the rhythm, of untamed, unshod feet!

But now —
It makes a man white-sick to see them now,
Dull — heads sagging — crowding to the trough —
No more spirit than a barren cow.
The well's pumped dry to wash poor fodder down,
Straw and salt — and endless salt and straw —
(Thank God the winter's mild so far)
Dry Russian thistle crackling in the jaw —

The old mare found the thistle pile, ate till she bulged,
Then, crazily, she wandered in the yard,
Saw a water-drum, and staggering to its rim,
Plodded around it — on and on in hard,
Madly relentless circle. Weaker — stumbling —
She fell quite suddenly, heaved once and lay.
(Nellie the kid's pet's gone, boys.
Hitch up the strongest team. Haul her away.
Maybe we should have mortgaged all we had
Though it wasn't much, even in good years, and draw
Ploughs with a jolting tractor.
Still — you can't make gas of thistles or oat-straw.)

VI

Relief.
"God, we tried so hard to stand alone!"

Relief.
"Well, we can't let the kids go cold."

They trudge away to school swinging half-empty
lard-pails,
to shiver in the schoolhouse (unpainted seven years),
learning from a blue-lipped girl
almost as starved as they.

Relief cars.
''Apples, they say, and clothes!''
The folks in town get their pick first,
Then their friends —
''Eight miles for us to go so likely we
won't get much —''
''Maybe we'll get the batteries charged up and have
the radio to kind of brighten things —''

Insurgents march in Spain

Japs bomb Chinese

Airliner lost

''Maybe we're not as badly off as some —''
''Maybe there'll be a war and we'll get paid to fight —''
''Maybe —''
''See if Eddie Cantor's on to-night!''

VII
People grew bored
Well-fed in the east and west
By stale, drought-area tales,
Bored by relief whinings,
Preferred their own troubles.
So those who still had stayed
On the scorched prairie,
Found even sympathy
Seeming to fail them
Like their own rainfall.

''Well — let's forget politics,
Forget the wind, our enemy!

Let's forget farming, boys,
Let's put on a dance tonight!
Mrs. Smith'll bring a cake.
Mrs. Olsen's coffee's swell!"

The small uneven schoolhouse floor
Scraped under big work-boots
Cleaned for the evening's fun,
Gasoline lamps whistled.
One Hungarian boy
Snapped at a shrill guitar,
A Swede from out north of town
Squeezed an accordion dry,
And a Scotchwoman from Ontario
Made the piano dance
In time to "The Mocking-Bird"
And "When I Grow too Old to Dream",
Only taking time off
To swing in a square-dance,
Between ten and half-past three.

Yet in the morning
Air peppered thick with dust,
All the night's happiness
Seemed far away, unreal
Like a lying mirage,
Or the icy-white glare
Of the alkali slough.

VIII

Presently the dark dust seemed to build a wall
That cut them off from east and west and north.
Kindness and honesty, things they used to know,
Seemed blown away and lost
In frantic soil.

At last they thought
Even God and Christ were hidden

By the false clouds.
— Dust-blinded to the staring parable,
Each wind-splintered timber like a pain-bent Cross.
Calloused, groping fingers, trembling
With overwork and fear,
Ceased trying to clutch at some faith in the dark,
Thin, sick courage fainted, lacking hope.
But tightened, tangled nerves scream to the brain
If there is no hope, give them forgetfulness!
The cheap light of the beer-parlour grins out,
Promising shoddy security for an hour.
The Finn who makes bad liquor in his barn
Grows fat on groaning emptiness of souls.

IX

The sun goes down. Earth like a thick black coin
Leans its round rim against the yellowed sky.
The air cools. Kerosene lamps are filled and lit
In dusty windows. Tired bodies crave to lie
In bed forever. Chores are done at last.
A thin horse neighs drearily. The chickens drowse,
Replete with grasshoppers that have gnawed and
scraped
Shrivelled garden-leaves. No sound from the gaunt
cows.

Poverty, hand in hand with fear, two great
Shrill-jointed skeletons stride loudly out
Across the pitiful fields, none to oppose.
Courage is roped with hunger, chained with doubt.
Only against the yellow sky, a part
Of the jetty silhouette of barn and house
Two figures stand, heads close, arms locked,
And suddenly some spirit seems to rouse
And gleam, like a thin sword, tarnished, bent,
But still shining in the spared beauty of moon,

As his strained voice says to her, "We're not licked
yet!
It must rain again — it *will!* Maybe — soon —"

X

Wind

in a lonely laughterless shrill game
with broken wash-boiler, bucket without
a handle, Russian thistle, throwing up
sections of soil.

God, will it never rain again? What about
those clouds out west? No, that's just dust, as thick
and stifling now as winter underwear.
No rain, no crop, no feed, no faith, only
wind.

City Heat Wave

Olive Nugent

The heat clings and presses,
Blanket heavy,
Picking with sweat wet fingers
At nerves
Stretched tight,
Snapping, shrilling,
At a word,
A look,
Soot dulled windows pushed high,
Splintered sills
Hot to the touch,
Tumbled sheets
Clinging to wet bodies
That toss and turn,

Toss and turn,
Until the smoke hazed dawn
Brings a fleeting coolness,
A breeze,
Racing the morning sun.

A Field of Wheat

Sinclair Ross

It was the best crop of wheat that John had ever grown; sturdy, higher than the knee, the heads long and filling well; a still, heat-hushed mile of it, undulating into a shimmer of summer-colts and crushed horizon blue. Martha finished pulling the little patch of mustard that John had told her about at noon, stood a minute with her shoulders strained back to ease the muscles that were sore from bending, then bunched up her apron filled with the yellow-blossomed weeds and started towards the road. She walked carefully, placing her feet edgeways between the rows of wheat to avoid trampling and crushing the stalks. The road was only a few rods distant, but several times she stopped before reaching it, holding her apron with one hand and with the other stroking the blades of grain that pressed close against her skirts, luxuriant and tall. Once she looked back, her eyes shaded, across the wheat to the dark fallow land beside it. John was there; she could see the long, slow-settling plume of dust thrown up by the horses and the harrow-cart. He was a fool for work, John. This year he was farming the whole section of land without help, managing with two outfits of horses, one for the morning and one for the afternoon; six, and sometimes even seven hours a shift.

It was John who gave such allure to the wheat. She thought of him hunched black and sweaty on the harrow-cart, twelve hours a day, smothering in dust, shoulders sagged wearily beneath the glare of sun. Her fingers touched the stalks of grain again and tightened on a supple blade until they made it squeak like a mouse. A crop like this was coming to him. He had had his share of failures and set-backs, if ever a man had, twenty times over.

Martha was thirty-seven. She had clinched with the body and substance of life; had loved, borne children — a boy had died — and yet the quickest aches of life, travail, heart-brokenness, they had never wrung as the wheat wrung. For the wheat allowed no respite. Wasting and unending it was struggle, struggle against wind and insects, drought and weeds. Not an heroic struggle to give a man courage and resolve, but a frantic, unavailing one. They were only poor, taunted, driven things; it was the wheat that was invincible. They only dreaded, built bright futures; waited for the first glint of green, watched timorous and eager while it thickened, merged, and at last leaned bravely to a ripple in the wind; then followed every slip of cloud into the horizon, turned to the wheat and away again. And it died tantalizingly sometimes, slowly: there would be a cool day, a pittance of rain.

Or perhaps it lived, perhaps the rain came, June, July, even into August, hope climbing, wish-patterns painted on the future. And then one day a clench and tremble to John's hand; his voice faltering, dull. Grasshoppers perhaps, sawflies or rust; no matter, they would grovel for a while, stand back helpless, then go on again. Go on in bitterness and cowardice, because there was nothing else but going-on.

She had loved John, for these sixteen years had stood close watching while he died — slowly, tantalizingly, as the parched wheat died. He had grown unkempt, ugly, morose. His voice was gruff, contentious, never broke into the deep, strong laughter that used to make her feel she was living at the heart of things. John was gone, love was gone; there was only wheat.

She plucked a blade; her eyes travelled hungrily up and down the field. Serene now, all its sting and torment sheathed.

Beautiful, more beautiful than Annabelle's poppies, than her sunsets. Theirs — all of it. Three hundred acres ready to give perhaps a little of what it had taken from her — John, his love, his lips unclenched.

Three hundred acres. Bushels, thousands of bushels, she wouldn't even try to think how many. And prices up this year. It would make him young again, lift his head, give him spirit. Maybe he would shave twice a week as he used to when they were first married, buy new clothes, believe in himself again.

She walked down the road towards the house, her steps quickening to the pace of her thoughts until the sweat clung to her face like little beads of oil. It was the children now, Joe and Annabelle: this winter perhaps they could send them to school in town and let them take music lessons. Annabelle, anyway. At a pinch Joe could wait a while; he was only eight. It wouldn't take Annabelle long to pick up her notes; already she played hymn tunes by ear on the organ. She was bright, a real little lady for manners; among town people she would learn a lot. The farm was no place to bring her up. Running wild and barefoot, what would she be like in a few years? Who would ever want to marry her but some stupid country lout?

John had never been to school himself; he knew what it meant to go through life with nothing but his muscles to depend upon; and that was it, dread that Annabelle and Joe would be handicapped as he was, that was what had darkened him, made him harsh and dour. That was why he breasted the sun and dust a frantic, dogged fool, to spare them, to help them to a life that offered more than sweat and debts. Martha knew. He was a slow, inarticulate man, but she knew. Sometimes it even vexed her, brought a wrinkle of jealousy, his anxiety about the children, his sense of responsibility where they were concerned. He never seemed to feel that he owed her anything, never worried about her future. She could sweat, grow flat-footed and shapeless, but that never bothered him.

Her thoughts were on their old, trudging way, the way they

always went; but then she halted suddenly, and with her eyes across the wheat again found freshening promise in its quiet expanse. The children must come first, but she and John — mightn't there be a little of life left for them too? A man was young at thirty-nine. And if she didn't have to work so hard, if she could get some new clothes, maybe some of the creams and things that other women had . . .

As she passed through the gate, Annabelle raced across the yard to meet her. ''Do you know what Joe's done? He's taken off all his clothes and he's in the trough with Nipper!'' She was a lanky girl, sunburned, barefoot, her face oval and regular, but spoiled by an expression that strained her mouth and brows into a reproachful primness. It was Martha who had taught her the expression, dinning manners and politeness into her, trying to make her better than the other little girls who went to the country school. She went on, her eyes wide and aghast, ''And when I told him to come out he stood right up, all bare, and I had to come away.''

''Well, you tell him he'd better be out before I get there.''

''But how can I tell him? He's all bare.''

Then Joe ran up, nothing on but little cotton knee-pants, strings of green scum from the water-trough still sticking to his face and arms. ''She's been peekin'.'' He pointed at Annabelle. ''Nipper and me just got into the trough to get cooled off, and she wouldn't mind her own business.''

''Don't you tell lies about me.'' Annabelle pounced on him and slapped his bare back. ''You're just a dirty little pig anyway, and the horses don't want to drink after you've been in the trough.''

Joe squealed, and excited by the scuffle Nipper yelled and spattered Martha with a spray of water from his coat and tail. She reached out to cuff him, missed, and then to satisfy the itch in her fingers seized Joe and boxed his ears. ''You put your shirt on and then go and pick peas for supper. Hurry now, both of you, and only the fat ones, mind. No, not you, Annabelle.''

There was something about Annabelle's face, burned and countrified, that changed Martha's mind. "You shell the peas when he gets them. You're in the sun too much as it is."

"But I've got a poppy out and if he goes to the garden by himself he'll pick it — just for spite." Annabelle spun round, and leaving the perplexity in her voice behind her, bolted for the garden. The next minute, before Martha had even reached the house, she was back again triumphant, a big fringed pink and purple poppy in her hand. Sitting down on the doorstep to admire the gaudy petals, she complained to herself, "They go so fast — the first little wind blows them all away." On her face, lengthening it, was bitten deeply the enigma of the flowers and the naked seedpods. Why did the beauty flash and the bony stalks remain?

Martha had clothes to iron, and biscuits to bake for supper; Annabelle and Joe quarrelled about the peas until she shelled them herself. It was hot — heat so intense and breathless that it weighed like a solid. An ominous darkness came with it, gradual and unnoticed. All at once she turned away from the stove and stood strained, inert. The silence seemed to gather itself, hold its breath. She tried to speak to Nipper and the children, all three sprawled in a heap alongside the house, but the hush over everything was like a raised finger, forbidding her.

A long immobile minute; suddenly a bewildering awareness that the light was choked; and then, muffled, still distant, but charged with resolution, climaxing the stillness, a slow, long brooding heave of thunder.

Martha darted to the door, stumbled down the step and around the corner of the house. To the west there was no sky, only a gulf of blackness, so black that the landscape seemed slipping down the neck of a funnel. Above, almost overhead, a heavy, hard-lined bank of cloud swept its way across the sun-white blue in august, impassive fury.

"Annabelle!" She wanted to scream a warning, but it was a

bare whisper. In front of her the blackness split — an abrupt, unforked gash of light as if angry hands had snatched to seal the rent.

"Annabelle! Quick — inside — !" Deep in the funnel shaggy thunder rolled, emerged and shook itself, then with hurtling strides leaped up to drum and burst itself on the advancing peak of cloud.

"Joe, come back here!" He was off in pursuit of Nipper, who had broken away from Annabelle when she tried to pull him into the house. "Before I warm you!"

Her voice broke. She stared into the blackness. There it was — the hail again — the same white twisting little cloud against the black one — just as she had seen it four years ago.

She craned her neck, looking to see whether John was coming. The wheat, the acres and acres of it, green and tall, if only he had put some insurance on it. Damned mule — just work and work. No head himself and too stubborn to listen to anyone else.

There was a swift gust of wind, thunder in a splintering avalanche, the ragged hail-cloud low and close. She wheeled, with a push sent Annabelle toppling into the house, and then ran to the stable to throw open the big doors. John would turn the horses loose — surely he would. She put a brace against one of the doors, and bashed the end into the ground with her foot. Surely — but he was a fool — such a fool at times. It would be just like him to risk a runaway for the sake of getting to the end of the field.

The first big drops of rain were spitting at her before she reached the house. Quietly, breathing hard, she closed the door, numb for a minute, afraid to think or move. At the other side of the kitchen Annabelle was tussling with Joe, trying to make him go down cellar with her. Frightened a little by her mother's excitement, but not really able to grasp the imminence of danger, she was set on exploiting the event; and to be compelled to seize her little brother and carry him down cellar struck her imagination as a superb way of crystallizing for all time the dreadfulness of the storm and her own dramatic part in it. But Martha shouted at her hoarsely, "Go and get pillows. Here, Joe, quick, up on the table." She snatched him off his feet and set him on the table beside the window. "Be ready now when the hail starts, to hold the pillow tight against the glass. You, Annabelle, stay upstairs at the west window in my room."

The horses were coming, all six at a break-neck gallop, terrified by the thunder and the whip stripes John had given them when he turned them loose. They swept past the house, shaking the earth, their harness jangling tinny against the brattle of thunder, and collided headlong at the stable door.

John, too; through Joe's legs Martha caught sight of his long, scarecrow shape stooped low before the rain. Distractedly, without purpose, she ran upstairs two steps at a time to Annabelle. "Don't be scared, here comes your father!" Her own voice shook, craven. "Why don't you rest your arms? It hasn't started yet."

As she spoke there was a sharp, crunching blow on the roof, its sound abruptly dead, sickening, like a weapon that has sunk deep into flesh. Wildly she shook her hands, motioning Annabelle back to the window, and started for the stairs. Again the blow came; then swiftly a stuttered dozen of them.

She reached the kitchen just as John burst in. With their eyes screwed up against the pommelling roar of the hail they stared at each other. They were deafened, pinioned, crushed. His face was a livid blank, one cheek smeared with blood where a jagged stone had struck him. Taut with fear, her throat aching, she turned away and looked through Joe's legs again. It was like a furious fountain, the stones bouncing high and clashing with those behind them. They had buried the earth, blotted out the horizon; there was nothing but their crazy spew of whiteness. She cowered away, put her hands to her ears.

Then the window broke, and Joe and the pillow tumbled off the table before the howling inrush of the storm. The stones clattered on the floor and bounded up to the ceiling, lit on the stove and threw out sizzling steam. The wind whisked pots and kettles off their hooks, tugged at and whirled the sodden curtains, crashed down a shelf of lamps and crockery. John pushed Martha and Joe into the next room and shut the door. There they found Annabelle huddled at the foot of the stairs, round-eyed, biting her nails in terror. The window she had been holding was broken too; and she had run away without closing the bedroom door, leaving a wild tide of wind upstairs to rage unchecked. It was rocking the whole house, straining at the walls. Martha ran up to close the door, and came down whimpering.

There was hail heaped on the bed, the pictures were blown off the walls and broken, the floor was swimming; the water would soak through and spoil all the ceilings.

John's face quietened her. They were crowded together, silent, averting their eyes from one another. Martha wanted to cry again, but dared not. Joe, awed to calmness, kept looking furtively at the trickle of blood on his father's face. Annabelle's eyes went wide and glassy as suddenly she began to wonder about Nipper. In the excitement and terror of the storm they had all forgotten him.

When at last they could go outside they stumbled over his body on the step. He had run away from Joe before the storm started, crawled back to the house when he saw John go in, and crouching down against the door had been beaten lifeless. Martha held back the children, while John picked up the mangled heap and hurried away with it to the stable.

Neither Joe nor Annabelle cried. It was too annihilating, too much like a blow. They clung tightly to Martha's skirts, staring across the flayed yard and garden. The sun came out, sharp and brilliant on the drifts of hail. There was an icy wind that made them shiver in their thin cotton clothes. "No, it's too cold on your feet." Martha motioned them back to the step as she started towards the gate to join John. ''I want to go with your father to look at the wheat. There's nothing anyway to see.''

Nothing but the glitter of sun on hailstones. Nothing but their wheat crushed into little rags of muddy slime. Here and there an isolated straw standing bolt upright in headless defiance. Martha and John walked to the far end of the field. There was no sound but their shoes slipping and rattling on the pebbles of ice. Both of them wanted to speak, to break the atmosphere of calamity that hung over them, but the words they could find were too small for the sparkling serenity of wasted field. Even as waste it was indomitable. It tethered them to itself, so that they could not feel or comprehend. It had come and gone, that was all; before its tremendousness and havoc they were prostrate. They had not yet risen to cry out or protest.

It was when they were nearly back to the house that Martha started to whimper. ''I can't go on any longer; I can't, John. There's no use, we've tried.'' With one hand she clutched him and with the other held her apron to her mouth. ''It's driving me out of my mind. I'm so tired — heartsick of it all. Can't you see?''

He laid his big hands on her shoulders. They looked at each other for a few seconds, then she dropped her head weakly against his greasy smock. Presently he roused her. ''Here come Joe and Annabelle!'' The pressure of his hands tightened. His bristly cheek touched her hair and forehead. ''Straighten up, quick, before they see you!''

It was more of him than she had had for years. ''Yes, John, I know — I'm all right now.'' There was a wistful little pull in her voice as if she would have had him hold her there, but hurriedly instead she began to dry her eyes with her apron. ''And tell Joe you'll get him another dog.''

Then he left her and she went back to the house. Mounting within her was a resolve, a bravery. It was the warming sunlight, the strength and nearness of John, a feeling of mattering, belonging. Swung far upwards by the rush and swell of recaptured life, she was suddenly as far above the desolation of the storm as a little while ago she had been abject before it. But in the house she was alone; there was no sunlight, only a cold wind through the broken window; and she crumpled again.

She tried to face the kitchen, to get the floor dried and the broken lamps swept up. But it was not the kitchen; it was tomorrow, next week, next year. The going on, the waste of life, the hopelessness.

Her hands fought the broom a moment, twisting the handle as if trying to unscrew the rusted cap of a jar; then abruptly she let it fall and strode outside. All very fine for John: he'd talk about education for Joe and Annabelle, and she could worry where the clothes were to come from so that they could go clean and decent even to the country school. It made no difference that she had wanted to take out hail insurance. He was the one that looked after things. She was just his wife; it wasn't for her to open her mouth. He'd pat her shoulder and let her come back to this. They'd be brave, go on again, forget about the crop. Go on, go on — next year and the next — go on till they were both ready for the scrap-heap. But she'd had enough. This time he'd go on alone.

Not that she meant it. Not that she failed to understand what John was going through. It was just rebellion. Rebellion because their wheat was beaten to the ground, because there was this brutal, callous finish to everything she had planned, because she had will and needs and flesh, because she was alive. Rebellion, not John at all — but how rebel against a summer storm, how find the throat of a cloud?

So at a jerky little run she set off for the stable, for John. Just that she might release and spend herself, no matter against whom or what, unloose the fury that clawed within her, strike back a blow for the one that had flattened her.

The stable was quiet, only the push of hay as the horses nosed through the mangers, the lazy rub of their flanks and hips against the stall partitions; and before its quietness her anger subsided, took time for breath. She advanced slowly, almost on tiptoe, peering past the horses' rumps for a glimpse of John. To the last stall, back again. And then there was a sound different from the stable sounds. She paused.

She had not seen him the first time she passed because he was pressed against one of the horses, his head pushed into the big deep hollow of its neck and shoulder, one hand hooked by the fingers in the mane, his own shoulders drawn up and shaking. She stared, thrust out her head incredulously, moved her lips, but stood silent. John sobbing there, against the horse. It was the strangest, most frightening moment of her life. He had always been so strong and grim; had just kept on as if he couldn't feel, as if there was a bull's hide over him, and now he was beaten.

She crept away. It would be unbearable to watch his humiliation if he looked up and saw her. Joe was wandering about the yard, thinking about Nipper and disconsolately sucking hailstones, but she fled past him, head down, stricken with guilty shame as if it were she who had been caught broken and afraid. He had always been so strong, a brute at times in his strength, and now —

Now — why now that it had come to this, he might never be able to get a grip of himself again. He might not want to keep on working, not if he were really beaten. If he lost heart, if he didn't care about Joe and Annabelle any more. Weeds and pests, drought and hail — it took so much fight for a man to hold his own against them all, just to hold his own, let alone make headway.

"Look at the sky!" It was Annabelle again, breathless and ecstatic. "The far one — look how it's opened like a fan!"

Withdrawn now in the eastern sky the storm clouds towered, gold-capped and flushed in the late sunlight, high still pyramids of snowiness and shadow. And one that Annabelle pointed to, apart, the farthest away of them all, this one in bronzed slow splendour spread up mountains high to a vast, plateau-like summit.

Martha hurried inside. She started the fire again, then nailed a blanket over the broken window and lit the big brass parlour lamp — the only one the storm had spared. Her hands were quick and tense. John would need a good supper tonight. The biscuits were water-soaked, but she still had the peas. He liked peas. Lucky that they had picked them when they did. This winter they wouldn't have so much as an onion or potato.

Hailstones and Character

Ken Wotherspoon

Whenever Mother cried it really broke me up. In spite of the insecure feeling her crying caused, however, there was a vindicatory need for me to make her cry some more. It's a strange contradiction but one that illustrates many of the paradoxical facets of human nature. Why does a person dread an unpleasant experience while at the same time setting up the machinery to duplicate the agony? It's my observation that this phenomenon is not so much a personality observation as it is an ego-punishing venture born out of the same psychological root as teasing and bullying.

We were very poor then but we kids didn't know it. Albert's folks were poor too and so were everybody else's. The conditioning was in progress that leads people to value material possessions. Because we had relatively few of these we were taught to respect property. Property was the means by which things got done hence it served basic human needs. Materialism was not one of the spiritual diseases rampant in those days but it was lying dormant until the next generation. People left property unprotected because it wasn't the end of life; it was a means to life and was there to be enjoyed in the community because of its scarcity. Property and goods were scarce but human resources were rich. Co-operatives, Credit Unions and the Wheat Pool were manifestations of this spirit.

It was not unnatural then for a farmer's wife like my mother to wait over long periods of time for some basic equipment like a new motor for the washing machine or even some new wash tubs or dishes or other everyday utensils. She had to know how to conserve and adjust the family needs to the available budget. She learned to sew not as a hobby but because of dire necessity; she cooked delicious meals not because she inherited the instinct but due to the hard facts that a little must be stretched a long way. That was when delicacies such as dandelion leaves and different ways of cooking wild meat were discovered. These taste-teasers found their way to the dining room table because they were available and cheap, not because of some health food fad. The children's clothes were best when they were done-over hand-me-downs. A second or third-hand pair of trousers displayed the mother's genius and creativity with a needle and therefore was worn with pride. Of course, when all your peers are engaged in similar pursuits in similar economic circumstances there's pretty good community spirit about. That's one reason Banner Hall community was such a jumping place.

But sometimes things got so bad that it made Mother cry. In the year that I passed into eighth grade it seemed as if Mom was going to get a few of the things she'd been waiting for. She needed and wanted a new sewing machine and a new cookstove for the kitchen. The repairman in Melville had fixed up the old Singer so often that he despaired each time he saw Mother coming into the shop.

"It's only going to give so many years service, ma'am, and then it just can't hold together. I'll give it another try but I really think you should consider my offer on a trade-in. I can give you a dandy that'll work trouble-free for years," he said one day when she came in.

"The way the crop's coming on this year I just may take you up on it, but until then . . . how about this spindle?" Mom was counting on that crop. She'd sell cream and eggs at the Co-op creamery but that would just about cover the flour and sugar and basic foodstuffs not to mention the material required for new clothes and new shoes for two of us kids. Running around barefoot most of the summer was okay but there were Sundays and winter to think about.

And the McClary range had just about had it. The fire box had been repaired so many times with hammered-out tomato tins that it rattled everytime we stuck a stick of wood in the fire. The right back lid had rusted off and it was supported by two bricks on that corner. Mom kept the oven and the surface of the lids shining by rubbing them down with wax paper but the stove was wearing out. She ranked its replacement high on the list of priorities for when the grain was threshed in the fall.

It was a promising year for wheat. Heavy snowfalls in the winter created a voluminous run-off in the spring. The ravines and streams overflowed their shallow banks, causing the sloughs and potholes to fill up to the brim. The water level was higher in the land than usual. Warm, drying winds created a good seedtime and June rains coming on the average of once a week had promoted heavy growth, supporting a long shot blade and the possibility of six-row heads on the wheat. The hay meadows were lush in growth. Prospects were for heavy yields on the summerfallow and abundance of feed for the cattle. Although the wetter than average soil encouraged the possibility of a cutworm outbreak there was little likelihood of the return of the grasshopper menace of the preceding year. The vicissitudes of farming, however, included a number of variables.

Mother ran from window to window whenever a rain cloud appeared. This served two purposes. There was her need to predict the direction and the amount of rainfall. She normally underestimated both of these items. Like anyone whose welfare is dependent upon visible but uncontrolled circumstances and elements there comes a feeling of helplessness and a kind of paranoia which you know is groundless yet somehow it haunts from deep down. Mother would see the cloud coming very close above our fence line even to the point of dropping its shield of water in such a manner that you could follow its direction. Then she would react as if some power above who controlled the system suddenly decided to tease her by pulling the cloud back or changing its direction to let it follow the fence line in a way that let the neighbour's land receive its benefits and passed by ours. We insisted usually that this wasn't the case but she'd remonstrate and say with feeling, "Oh, what's the use. They're getting it over there and we're going to miss it again. Oh, it's maddening." Then it would open up and rain.

Her other need was to check the cloud for the dangerous white and green color denoting hail in the storm. This was a dreadful sight to Mother. When it appeared it was usually in the late afternoon on a hot, humid day while Dad was still out in one of the fields. She had to deal with it alone. We kids were not much help because in the first place we kind of enjoyed a real storm with lightning, thunder, torrential rain and large hailstones. We liked to go to school the next day and out-boast each other. "They were as large as golf balls at our place" or "Heck, we had some as big as goose eggs" and so on. We knew something of the destructiveness of hail and the loss of crops but we didn't have to make the crucial decisions about what we'd do to survive afterwards. That's what parents were for. Mother had to run from window to window to anticipate whether the storm was a friend or a foe. And by the same mystic insight that told her how the neighbors got most of the rain she was able to foresee how if there was a hail streak in the cloud it would be headed straight for our crops. Having no hail insurance and knowing how good things could be if we got this bumper crop off combined to make my folks very jumpy this summer.

July so far had been unusually hot. The foliage everywhere

was responding to the ideal growing conditions. Hay fields and meadows had been cleared of their verdant production and were going in for second growth. The wheat waved various shades of green in the fields as the blossoms were leaving the richly filling heads: oats and barley crops foretokened feed bins full of the stuff that fattens the shorthorns and Herefords and helps replenish the milk of Holstein cows. The garden beside the house was beautiful in its potential stock of vegetables for the basement.

A distant flash of lightning streaking down from a huge thunderhead in the west announced the approach of a refreshing summer shower. I was feeding the chickens when I saw it. In a few moments a faraway subdued growl followed as the thunder resounded across the empty sky. The easterly breeze ceased its blowing. A peaceful quiet descended on the entire farm as the huge cloud began to blank out the direct effects of the blistering hot sun. It was so quiet that I could hear Dad's voice a mile away as he guided the six horse outfit from the east of the cultivator. "C'mon, Trixie, Pat, C'mon; Gee, Haw" and so on. The scraping of the cultivator tooth over a rock seemed to bring him right into the yard. Cows munching grass near the dugout created a soft, tearing sound that added to the aura of peacefulness in the moments before the wind started to pick up again. Mother was hoeing in the garden and she called out,

"Isn't that storm approaching awfully fast?" I watched the amazing configurations of cloud design change as streaks of black folded over its crisp outer edges and striations of light, black and grey wove an interlaced pattern across the centre of the formation which seemed to be the beginning of two clouds melting together. Chain lightning crisscrossed and was intercepted by the bolts of fork lightning slamming prodigious amounts of energy into the ground. The cloud was growing as it approached. Although we were in an area devoid of wind it was obvious there was a massive force pushing the storm towards us. The sound of the thunder now echoed across the fields and bounced from bush to bush. The brightness that had enshrouded us a few minutes earlier was being transformed into a charcoalish effect so that the outlines of the hills and the buildings were becoming hazy as at dusk. The peak of the cloud was arching above us. Now the leaves began a faint rustle, gradually growing in intensity until I could feel the hot rush of moving air brush my cheeks. Dust whipped around in little eddies at several places in the barnyard as if set off by a central signal. The chickens, which had been oblivious to the change while they pecked the grain I was scattering, began to cackle up a chorus and move towards the chicken house. Mother called,

"We'd better get to the house! Where are the others?" Then as was her custom she raised her bandannaed head and cupped her hands over her mouth and ran through the names of my brothers and sisters she knew to be in the vicinity at the time. We ran to the house even as the wind whipped the iron gate on the yard fence back and forth and sent some spilled straw swirling over our heads.

Mother started the pre-storm ritual.

"Close those upstairs windows. Shut the front door. Let that darned dog in." Jet was scratching at the back door which we'd closed as the last one arrived. She went to the west window and said, "That's a mean one coming. Wonder if it'll get time to drop any rain or will it just blow on by?" Then she scurried through the dining room and turned right to get a view of the south of us.

"Look at that! Kosha's are going to get it the heaviest again. Just look at that dust cloud. And wow! see that lightning." We all interchanged stations at the various windows. Some upstairs and some down. Giggling and pushing and complaining about the others' elbows, we jockeyed for the best spots; hoping to catch sight of the mightiest lightning flash and see the first huge splats of water as the rain blotted into the dust. "Oh dear, look at that ugly white strip!" Her voice sounded ominous. Near the core of the cloud, masses of black and blue cascaded over and over creating a waterfall effect. Just below this marvelous cyclorama a definite outline of a peculiar characteristic of such storms coalescing on hot, humid days was taking its portentous shape. A greenish, yellow streak was rapidly descending. Near the point of this phenomenon its edges were well-defined but irregular. At its base point a whitish purple indicated its depth and abundant resources. It was the dreaded hail strip. It might be a half mile or more wide. If it came down it would dump its ravaging load mercilessly on the greenery and the buildings and strive to wipe out as much as nature would allow.

Enormous drops of water bounced off the roof of the back porch. A darkened room and a blinding flash of light proclaimed the cloud opening upon us. Torrents of water slid down the west side of our house as the gale force winds ripped through the cloud's centre. Little troughs along the garden path filled up and overflowed, the lawn became a shimmering lake in a few minutes. Mother went into the back porch. I followed her because I knew I couldn't get hurt by her side. Her face showed a strain that wasn't there earlier. Before I could ask her what was wrong, nature itself announced it.

The roof above us began to bang and crackle as the first hailstones came down. Hailstones falling without a wind pushing them do not carry the devastation that these carried. The wind smashed them into the ground and rolled them across its surface. Lightning seemed to originate all around us in the west, the east, the north and south. One crack of thunder roared into the next as the sky unleashed a fury of recrimination as savage as a giant gone mad. What a sharp contrast to the stifling calm preceding this galloping storm!

"Oh my God, please, no, don't let it!" Mother was calling as if the storm had ears. And as if in arrogant answer to a helpless plea it responded with more wind, more velocity and noise. The hail cascaded down. "Merciful Lord, no; don't let it happen. Think of the children, the long winter. O God, no!" Mother repeated as if to challenge the whole existence. It seemed so futile. So lonely. The ground was covered now with varied chunks and shapes of ice, the smaller pieces whirling around in the little rivulets and pools, the larger ones stuck in ugly patterns across the ground. The wind raged on and more ice-spiked rain hurtled down. My Mother now was quiet but troubled-looking. She didn't go back into the house, she just stared despairingly out the door of that back kitchen as we sometimes called it.

In a few moments it was all over. An icy chill surrounded us. It was quiet again except for the gurgling sounds of the hundreds of little rivers created by the preceding outbreak.

"Mom, look at those stones!" I shouted as I ran in bare feet to retrieve some of the icy giants. She didn't seem to hear me as she passed by me and went out the gate towards the wheat field back of the barn where one of our best stands of wheat was growing. It was in that direction that Dad would be coming home. I followed a short distance behind her. I sensed somehow that this was going to be a very bad moment.

She seemed taller as she walked erectly towards the gate of the field. It was set between two poplar bluffs. She was beautiful as she walked ahead of me. There was an air of grace and elegance about her which I felt as she moved some distance ahead of me. What she was thinking or where she was going I couldn't be sure. She appeared to be lighter than before. Her feet hardly made prints in the mud. With her head high she adeptly dropped the barbed wire gate and walked part way into the field. I stopped in my tracks. The beautiful flowing waves of wheat had been smashed and broken into the soil. Even the lumps of dirt and stones showed above the demolished plants. It was all over.

Mother stood there for a long while. I didn't know what to do or what to say. I stuck to my tracks and felt terribly upset. She just stood there looking across the field with her elbows arched out and her hands on her hips. Then after what seemed to me to be a long time, she turned slightly towards me but didn't see me. Her body wilted a little from its beautiful poise and she walked slowly and resolutely over to a large poplar tree. Forgetting where she was and who she was she looped her arms around that tree and sort of hung to one side letting her head rest against the tree's trunk. Her body started to shake and quiver. Then I could hear her cry. I felt terrible. I had to look back towards the house. Then I turned to face her again when I heard another voice. Dad had come to her and he had both his arms around her. I heard him say,

"There, there, it's going to be all right, Beckie, don't cry." That was a name I guess he used for her when they were young lovers. He used that name often when he thought we kids wouldn't hear. I knew that he was using it now because he knew how hard things really were for Mom and for all of us. There would be no new sewing machine; no new stove.

I repeat a question I started with. Why does a person dread an unpleasant experience like this while at the same time setting off the machinery to duplicate the agony?

As it turned out, our crop was a hundred percent loss on the half section near the house including, of course, the quarter on which the homestead was located. Only a small portion of the wheat and oats had been struck by this storm on land we owned a half mile north of the house. This was some consolation as it meant that unless another storm hit prior to harvest, the heavy rain accompanying this storm would assure a fairly heavy yield in that half section.

One hot afternoon several days later another less vicious looking storm appeared from the southwest. Mother was in the back kitchen preserving saskatoon berries. She had a tub of water boiling on the old cookstove and couldn't leave it to take up her lookout positions in the house. There were streaks of lightning and rumbles of thunder but not of the threatening quality of the ruinous storm that visited our place earlier.

"How does it look?" she called out to me.

“I think it looks bad, Mom!” I shouted in return from the top of the little hill in the backyard. Actually I knew I was exaggerating and I was aware that Mother could not join me or verify my reports at this juncture. But I persisted in perpetrating one of the foulest kinds of fabrication. One couldn’t classify this as teasing; it was juvenile maliciousness.

Thunder growled closer and closer. The trees around the house began their ritual dance. There would be a nice summer shower but not a dangerous storm. I was certain of this but I continued my embellished deceptiveness. Moving nearer to the house I called out,

“There’s a nasty white and green streak heading right over us.” Just as I said this some large drops of rain started to fall and the wind picked up a little.

“Oh, Mom, here it comes,” I shouted. To my disgust and shame I report that I had picked up a handful of small stones and started casting them, singly, then two and three at a time, on the shingled roof above my Mother’s head. The rain began to fall in a fairly heavy shower. The combined effects of the stones rolling off the roof and the gentle rain that was falling caused my Mother to drop whatever she was doing and rush to the door. I was caught in the act performing a deed that has never brought much satisfaction to my memory of that particular day.

We are born with the potential of being either very loving or becoming very cruel. Along the way we decide which it will be for us. Fortunate are the children who recognize these latent powers early enough to be able to isolate the alternatives. Of course, good mothers and fathers help.

Autumn

Margot Osborn

Autumn is an old brave, loping along
in beaded moccasins.
The mischievous winds
are tearing down his painted tepee;
but he is headed South, long braids flying,
and the sun glinting on his gaudy head feathers.

This Valley

Myrna Harvey

In this valley wide and deep
  The snow is drifted high;
The air is cold and sharp as ice;
  Darkness rules the sky.

The cold and lonely, whining wind
  Sings its sad refrain,
And bends and breaks the brittle boughs
  Which moan as if in pain.

And on the hills the snow lies deep,
  Bleak, and cold, and white
While fenceposts line the barren fields;
  There is no life in sight.

The only sound is of the wind;
  The only sight is white;
The only feeling is the cold:
  Tonight.

The Frost

George Bowering

But the morning
hoar frost

the breath of cold birds
on trees

the metal of January
in this place.

The crystals, white
hanging from the iron handrail

cold to fingers
sweet to taste.

Lanterns

Andrew Suknaski

the blizzard came
after the first frost —
the hired man left the house
with a lantern
to see how the cattle
were taking the storm
in the north pasture
my father found him
three days later
near the fence on the east side
of the pasture

the faithful dog froze
beside him — curled up
like a lover in the man's arms

(the broken lantern
lay near a stone   the glass shattered)

men freeze this way everywhere
when lanterns fall   a p a r t
(even within one's arms
inside the city's rim)

Snow

Frederick Philip Grove

Towards morning the blizzard had died down, though it was still far from daylight. Stars without number blazed in the dark blue sky which presented that brilliant and uncompromising appearance always characterizing, on the northern plains of America, those nights in the dead of winter when the thermometer dips to its lowest levels.

In the west Orion was sinking to the horizon. It was between five and six o'clock.

In the bush-fringe of the Big Marsh, sheltered by thick but bare bluffs of aspens, stood a large house, built of logs, whitewashed, solid — such as a settler who is still single would put up only when he thinks of getting married. It, too, looked ice-cold, frozen in the night. Not a breath stirred where it stood; a thin thread of whitish smoke, reaching up to the level of the tree-tops, seemed to be suspended into the chimney rather than to issue from it.

Through the deep snow of the yard, newly packed, a man was fighting his way to the door. Arrived there, he knocked and knocked, first tapping with his knuckles, then hammering with his fists.

Two, three minutes passed. Then a sound awoke in the house, as of somebody stirring, getting out of bed.

The figure on the door-slab — a medium-sized, slim man in sheepskin and high rubber boots into which his trousers were tucked, with the ear-flaps of his cap pulled down — stood and waited, bent over, hands thrust into the pockets of the short coat, as if he wished to shrink into the smallest possible space so as to offer the smallest possible surface to the attack of the cold. In order to get rid of the dry, powdery snow which filled every crease of his footgear and trousers, he stamped his feet. His chin was drawn deep into the turned-up collar on whose points his breath had settled in the form of a thick layer of hoarfrost.

At last a bolt was withdrawn inside.

The face of a man peered out, just discernible in the starlight.

Then the door was opened; in ominous silence the figure from the outside entered, still stamping its feet.

Not a word was spoken till the door had been closed. Then a voice sounded through the cold and dreary darkness of the room.

"Redcliff hasn't come home. He went to town about noon and expected to get back by midnight. We're afraid he's lost."

The other man, quite invisible in the dark, had listened, his teeth chattering with the cold. "Are you sure he started out from town?"

"Well," the new-comer answered hesitatingly, "one of the horses came to the yard."

"One of his horses?"

"Yes. One of those he drove. The woman worked her way to my place to get help."

The owner of the house did not speak again. He went, in the dark, to the door in the rear and opened it. There, he groped about for matches and, finding them, lighted a lamp. In the room stood a big stove, a coal-stove of the self-feeder type; but the fuel used was wood. He opened the drafts and shook the grate clear of ashes; there were two big blocks of spruce in the fire-box, smouldering away for the night. In less than a minute they blazed up.

The new-comer entered, blinking in the light of the lamp, and looked on. Before many minutes the heat from the stove began to tell.

"I'll call Bill," the owner of the house said. He was himself of medium height or only slightly above it, but of enormous breadth of shoulder; a figure built for lifting loads. By his side the other man looked small, weakly, dwarfed.

He left the room and, returning through the cold, bare hall in front, went upstairs.

A few minutes later a tall, slender, well-built youth bolted into the room where the new-comer was waiting. Bill, Carroll's hired man, was in his underwear and carried his clothes, thrown in a heap over his arm. Without loss of time, but jumping, stamping, swinging his arms, he began at once to dress.

He greeted the visitor. "Hello, Mike! What's that Abe tells me? Redcliff got lost?"

"Seems that way," said Mike listlessly.

"By gringo," Bill went on, "I shouldn't wonder. In that storm I'd have waited in town! Wouldn't catch me going out in that kind of weather!"

"Didn't start till late in the afternoon," Mike Sobotski said in his shivering way.

"No. And didn't last long either," Bill agreed while he shouldered into his overalls. "But while she lasted . . ."

At this moment Abe Carroll, the owner of the farm, re-entered, with sheepskin, fur cap, and long woollen scarf on his arm. His deeply lined, striking, square face bore a settled frown while he held the inside of his sheepskin to the stove, to warm it up. Then, without saying a word, he got deliberately into it.

Mike Sobotski still stood bent over, shivering, though he

had opened his coat and, on his side of the stove, was catching all the heat it afforded.

Abe, with the least motion needed to complete dressing, made for the door. In passing Bill, he flung out an elbow which touched the young man's arm. "Come on," he said; and to the other, pointing to the stove, "Close the drafts."

A few minutes later a noise as of rearing and snorting horses in front of the house. . . .

Mike, buttoning up his coat and pulling his mitts over his hands, went out.

They mounted three unsaddled horses. Abe leading, they dashed through the new drifts in the yard and out through the gate to the road. Here, where the shelter of the bluffs screening the house was no longer effective, a light but freshening breeze from the north-west made itself felt as if fine little knives were cutting into the flesh of their faces.

Abe dug his heels into the flank of his rearing mount. The horse was unwilling to obey his guidance, for Abe wanted to leave the road and to cut across wild land to the south-west.

The darkness was still inky black, though here and there, where the slope of the drifts slanted in the right direction, starlight was dimly reflected from the snow. The drifts were six, eight, in places ten feet high; and the snow was once more crawling up their flanks, it was so light and fine. It would fill the tracks in half an hour. As the horses plunged through, the crystals dusted up in clouds, flying aloft over horses and riders.

In less than half an hour they came to a group of two little buildings, of logs, that seemed to squat on their haunches in the snow. Having entered the yard through a gate, they passed one of the buildings and made for the other, a little stable; their horses snorting, they stopped in its lee.

Mike dismounted, throwing the halter-shank of his horse to Bill. He went to the house, which stood a hundred feet or so away. The shack was even smaller than the stable, twelve by fifteen feet perhaps. From its flue-pipe a thick, white plume of smoke blew to the south-east.

Mike returned with a lantern; the other two sprang to the ground; and they opened the door to examine the horse which the woman had allowed to enter.

The horse was there, still excited, snorting at the leaping light and shadows from the lantern, its eyes wild, its nostrils dilated. It was covered with white frost and fully harnessed, though its traces were tied up to the back-band.

"He let him go," said Mike, taking in these signs. "Must have stopped and unhitched him."

"Must have been stuck in a drift," Bill said, assenting.

"And tried to walk it," Abe added.

For a minute or so they stood silent, each following his own gloomy thoughts. Weird, luminous little clouds issued fitfully from the nostrils of the horse inside.

"I'll get the cutter," Abe said at last.

"I'll get it," Bill volunteered. "I'll take the drivers along. We'll leave the filly here in the stable."

"All right."

Bill remounted, leading Abe's horse. He disappeared into the night.

Abe and Mike, having tied the filly and the other horse in their stalls, went out, closed the door, and turned to the house.

There, by the light of a little coal-oil lamp, they saw the woman sitting at the stove, pale, shivering, her teeth achatter, trying to warm her hands, which were cold with fever, and looking with lack-lustre eyes at the men as they entered.

The children were sleeping; the oldest, a girl, on the floor, wrapped in a blanket and curled up like a dog; four others in one narrow bed, with hay for a mattress, two at the head, two at the foot; the baby on, rather than in, a sort of cradle made of a wide board slung by thin ropes to the pole-roof of the shack.

The other bed was empty and unmade. The air was stifling from a night of exhalations.

"We're going to hunt for him," Mike said quietly. "We've sent for a cutter. He must have tried to walk."

The woman did not answer. She sat and shivered.

"We'll take some blankets," Mike went on. "And some whisky if you've got any in the house."

He and Abe were standing by the stove, opposite the woman, and warming their hands, their mitts held under their armpits.

The woman pointed with a look to a home-made little cupboard nailed to the wall and apathetically turned back to the stove. Mike went, opened the door of the cupboard, took a bottle from it, and slipped it into the pocket of his sheepskin. Then he raised the blankets from the empty bed, rolled them roughly into a bundle, dropped it, and returned to the stove where, with stiff fingers, he fell to rolling a cigarette.

Thus they stood for an hour or so.

Abe's eye was fastened on the woman. He would have liked to say a word of comfort, of hope. What was there to be said?

She was the daughter of a German settler in the bush, some six or seven miles north-east of Abe's place. Her father, an oldish, unctuous, bearded man, had, some ten years ago, got tired of the hard life in the bush where work meant clearing, picking stones, and digging stumps. He had sold his homestead and bought a prairie-farm, half a section, on crop-payments, giving notes for the equipment which he needed to handle the place. He had not been able to make a "go". His bush farm had fallen back on his hands; he had lost his all and returned to the place. He had been counting on the help of his two boys — big, strapping young fellows — who were to clear much land and to raise crops which would lift the debt. But the boys had refused to go back to the bush; they could get easy work in town. Ready money would help. But the ready money had melted away in their hands. Redcliff, the old people's son-in-law, had been their last hope. They were on the point of losing even their bush farm. Here they might perhaps still have found a refuge for their old age — though Redcliff's homestead lay on the sandflats bordering on the marsh where the soil was thin, dreadfully thin; it drifted when the scrub-brush was cleared off. Still, with Redcliff living, this place had been a hope. What were they to do if he was gone? And this woman, hardly more than a girl, in spite of her six children!

The two tiny, square windows of the shack began to turn grey.

At last Abe, thinking he heard a sound, went to the door and stepped out. Bill was there; the horses were shaking the snow out of their pelts; one of them was pawing the ground.

Once more Abe opened the door and gave Mike a look for a signal. Mike gathered the bundle of blankets into his arms, pulled on his mitts, and came out.

Abe reached for the lines, but Bill objected.

"No. Let me drive. I found something."

And as soon as the two older men had climbed in, squeezing into the scant space on the seat, he clicked his tongue.

"Get up there!" he shouted, hitting the horses' backs with his lines. And with a leap they darted away.

Bill turned, heading back to the Carroll farm. The horses plunged, reared, snorted, and then, throwing their heads, shot along in a gallop, scattering snow-slabs right and left and throwing wing-waves of the fresh, powdery snow, especially on the lee side. Repeatedly they tried to turn into the wind, which they were cutting at right angles. But Bill plied the whip and guided them expertly.

Nothing was visible anywhere; nothing but the snow in the first grey of dawn. Then, like enormous ghosts, or like evanescent apparitions, the trees of the bluff were adumbrated behind the lingering veils of the night.

Bill turned to the south, along the straight trail which bordered Abe Carroll's farm. He kept looking out sharply to right and left. But after awhile he drew his galloping horses in.

"Whoa!" he shouted, rearing at the lines in seesaw fashion. And when the rearing horses came to a stop, excited and breathless, he added, "I've missed it." He turned.

"What is it?" Abe asked.

"The other horse," Bill answered. "It must have had the scent of our yard. It's dead . . . frozen stiff."

A few minutes later he pointed to a huge white mound on top of a drift to the left. "That's it," he said, turned the horses into the wind, and stopped.

To the right, the bluffs of the farm slowly outlined themselves in the morning greyness.

The two older men alighted and, with their hands, shovelled the snow away. There lay the horse, stiff and cold, frozen into a rock-like mass.

"Must have been here a long while," Abe said.

Mike nodded. "Five, six hours." Then he added, "Couldn't have had the smell of the yard. Unless the wind has turned."

"It has," Abe answered, and pointed to a fold in the flank of the snow-drift which indicated that the present drift had been superimposed on a lower one whose longitudinal axis ran to the north-east.

For a moment longer they stood and pondered.

Then Abe went back to the cutter and reached for the lines. "I'll drive," he said.

Mike climbed in.

Abe took his bearings, looking for landmarks. They were only two or three hundred feet from his fence. That enabled him to estimate the exact direction of the breeze. He clicked his tongue. "Get up!"

And the horses, catching the infection of a dull excitement, shot away. They went straight into the desert of drifts to the west, plunging ahead without any trail, without any landmark in front to guide them.

They went for half an hour, an hour, and longer.

None of the three said a word. Abe knew the sandflats better than any other; Abe reasoned better than they. If anyone could find the missing man, it was Abe.

Abe's thought ran thus. The horse had gone against the wind. It would never have done so without good reason; that reason could have been no other than a scent to follow. If that was so, however, it would have gone in as straight a line as it could. The sandflats stretched away to the south-west for sixteen miles with not a settlement, not a farm but Redcliff's. If Abe managed to strike that line of scent, it must take him to the point whence the horses had started.

Clear and glaring, with an almost indifferent air, the sun rose to their left.

And suddenly they saw the wagon-box of the sleigh sticking out of the snow ahead of them.

Abe stopped, handed Bill the lines, and got out. Mike followed. Nobody said a word.

The two men dug the tongue of the vehicle out of the snow and tried it. This was part of the old, burnt-over bush land south of the sandflats. The sleigh was tightly wedged in between several charred stumps which stuck up through the snow. That was the reason why the man had unhitched the horses and turned them loose. What else, indeed, could he have done?

The box was filled with a drift which, toward the tail-gate, was piled high, for there three bags of flour were standing on end and leaning against a barrel half-filled with small parcels, the interstices between which were packed with mealy snow.

Abe waded all around the sleigh, reconnoitring; and as he did so, wading at the height of the upper-edge of the wagon-box, the snow suddenly gave way beneath him; he broke in; the drift was hollow.

A suspicion took hold of him; with a few quick reaches of his arm he demolished the roof of the drift all about.

And there, in the hollow, lay the man's body as if he were sleeping, a quiet expression, as of painless rest, on his face. His eyes were closed; a couple of bags were wrapped about his shoulders. Apparently he had not even tried to walk! Already chilled to the bone, he had given in to that desire for rest, for shelter at any price, which overcomes him who is doomed to freeze.

Without a word the two men carried him to the cutter and laid him down on the snow.

Bill, meanwhile, had unhitched the horses and was hooking them to the tongue of the sleigh. The two others looked on in silence. Four times the horses sprang, excited because Bill tried to make them pull with a sudden twist. The sleigh did not stir.

"Need an axe," Mike said at last, "to cut the stumps. We'll get the sleigh later."

Mike hitched up again and turned the cutter. The broken snowdrifts through which they had come gave the direction.

Then they laid the stiff, dead body across the floor of their vehicle, leaving the side-doors open for it protruded both ways. They themselves climbed up on the seat and crouched down, so as not to put their feet on the corpse.

Thus they returned to Abe Carroll's farm where, still in silence, they deposited the body in the granary.

That done, they stood for a moment as if in doubt. Then Bill unhitched the horses and took them to the stable to feed.

"I'll tell the woman," said Mike. "Will you go tell her father?"

Abe nodded. "Wait for breakfast," he added.

It was ten o'clock; and none of them had eaten since the previous night.

On the way to Altmann's place in the bush, drifts were no obstacles to driving. Drifts lay on the marsh, on the open sand-flats.

Every minute of the time Abe, as he drove along, thought of that woman in the shack: the woman, alone, with six children, and with the knowledge that her man was dead.

Altmann's place in the bush looked the picture of peace and

comfort: a large log-house of two rooms. Window-frames and doors were painted green. A place to stay with, not to leave. . . .

When Abe knocked, the woman, whom he had seen but once in his life, at the sale where they had lost their possessions, opened the door — an enormously fat woman, overflowing her clothes. The man, tall, broad, with a long, rolling beard, now grey, stood behind her, peering over her shoulder. A visit is an event in the bush!

"Come in," he said cheerfully when he saw Abe. "What a storm that was!"

Abe entered the kitchen which was also dining- and living-room. He sat down on the chair which was pushed forward for him and looked at the two old people, who remained standing.

Suddenly, from the expression of his face, they anticipated something of his message. No use dissembling.

"Redcliff is dead," he said. "He was frozen to death last night on his way home from town."

The two old people also sat down; it looked as if their knees had given way beneath them. They stared at him, dumbly, a sudden expression of panic fright in their eyes.

"I thought you might want to go to your daughter," Abe added sympathetically.

The man's big frame seemed to shrink as he sat there. All the unctuousness and the conceit of the handsome man dwindled out of his bearing. The woman's eyes had already filled with tears.

Thus they remained for two, three minutes.

Then the woman folded her fat, pudgy hands; her head sank low on her breast; and she sobbed, "God's will be done!"

Carrion Spring

Wallace Stegner

Often in Saskatchewan a man awakens on a winter night hearing a great wind, and his heart sinks at the prospect of more shut-in days, more cold, difficulty, discomfort, and danger. But one time in ten, something keeps him from burrowing back under his blankets, something keeps him suspiciously on his elbow, straining his ears for the sounds of hope. Repudiating his hope even while he indulges it, he may leave the warmth of bed and go to the door, bracing himself for the needles of thirty below. And one time in ten, when he opens door and storm door against the grab and bluster of the wind, the air rushes in his face as warm as milk, all but smelling of orange blossoms, and he dances a caper on his cold floor and goes back to bed knowing that in the two or three days that the chinook blows it will gulp all the snow except the heaviest drifts and leave the prairie dry enough to sit down on. Dozing off, he hears the crescendo of drip, the slump of heavied snow on the roof, the crash of loosened icicles under the eaves.

Several times every winter the harsh Saskatchewan weather is relieved by that beautiful mild wind that can raise the temperature in a half hour from zero to fifty above. It is the chinook that makes Saskatchewan bearable in winter, the chinook that clears the prairies periodically and allows cattle to feed. It was a chinook that the cattle outfits on the Whitemud waited for in vain during the winter of 1906-07.

In vain, or nearly. November, December, January, brought them only blizzards, cold snaps, freezing fogs, snow. A forkful at a time, the T-Down boys fed the hay they had stacked at Bates and Stonepile. They broke down their ponies trying to drag clear patches of hillside where the cattle could feed, only to see new snow cover their work, or the cattle flinching back from the wind to gnaw willows and starve in the snowy bottoms. Not until the end of January did the punchers at Bates and Stonepile feel on their faces that soft and strengthening blast from the southwest. They went to bed drunk on it, assured that though hundreds of cattle were dead along the river, something could be saved. When they awoke in the morning the air was still, the abortive chinook had died, the snow that had been thawed mushy was frozen hard again, the prairie was sheathed in four inches of solid ice, and cattle that had lain down in the snow were frozen in, unable to move. They dragged free as many as they could reach, threw open the gates on whatever scraps of hay were left, and retreated to the ranch, which was hoarding its few stacks for the ultimate emergency. The emergency arrived, or rather continued. Storm and cold through February; then a chinook that gave the scarecrow survivors a few days of relief; then more blizzards and cold that locked them in ice until May. During the last six weeks they could do nothing but skin out the dead.

Their story goes on too long; it is nothing but unrelieved hardship, failure, death, gloom. Even the wolfer Schulz, who had no concern about cattle, shared the ruin of that winter. The wolves that he would ordinarily have run down with his hounds on the flats were all down in the deep snow of the bottoms, where the cattle were and where their big pads would let them run while a hound floundered. They sat just out of rifle range and laughed; they were so well fed and so smart they never went near the traps Schulz set. In February, furious and frustrated, without a single wolf to show for months of effort, Schulz locked up his hounds in the Stonepile stable and poisoned a dozen carcasses up and down the river. But his great staghound, Puma, was too much of a pet to stay locked in. He broke out one afternoon when Schulz was gone, followed his master's tracks several miles up-river, stopped on the way to feed on one of the poisoned carcasses, and came upon Schultz in the middle of a white-out, dense freezing fog, where the wolfer had built a fire on the ice to keep warm until he could get his bearings. For an hour or two the hound padded back and forth with the man as he walked to keep from freezing around the little fire of willows. Then the dog began acting strange, rolling, gaping; and at some moment during the night, lost in the wilderness of that lost river, sick and furious at his winter's failure, the wolfer looked up and saw the hound coming for him. He jumped to his gun, stuck butt down in the snow, and killed the dog with one shot in the mouth.

No one saw Schulz again. He simply vanished, disappointed or crazy or fed up. Several months later the T-Down boys, conducting their pitiful spring roundup of survivors, heard how he drowned swimming his horse across the Milk River in the spring break-up.

A casualty, a wild man defeated by the wild. But the civilized did no better. And especially Molly Henry, who on her wedding day in late October had said goodby to whatever civilization was offered by her home town of Malta, Montana, and who except for the Christmas blowout had enjoyed neither fun nor the company of another woman since. She was a tough and competent little body; she believed in work as a cure for the doldrums, and she had married with the full intention of being a good wife to a cattleman. Among the things she and Ray had talked about on their buckboard honeymoon were the future settlement of that country and the opportunities open to the young and industrious.

But six months is a long time to be shut in, too long a stretch of desperate work and hardship and shortages and unmitigated failure. The brief dream of Indian Summer would not have lasted through all that disastrous winter. In spite of the work she used as therapy, hope would have festered in her. When the long agony finally broke, and the thaw began, and the sun that had seemed gone forever came back in spells of unbelievable warmth, she would have greeted release with a tight mouth, determined to take her man and her marriage back where there was a chance for both.

The moment she came to the door she could smell it, not really rotten and not coming from any particular direction, but sweetish, faintly sickening, sourceless, filling the whole air the way a river's water can taste of weeds — the carrion smell of a whole country breathing out in the first warmth across hundreds of square miles.

Three days of chinook had uncovered everything that had been under snow since November. The yard lay discolored and ugly, gray ashpile, rusted cans, spilled lignite, bones. The clinkers that had given them winter footing to privy and stable lay in raised gray wavers across the mud; the strong lariats they had used for lifelines in blizzardy weather had dried out and sagged to the ground. Muck was knee deep down in the corrals by the sod-roofed stable, the whitewashed logs were yellowed at the corners from dogs lifting their legs against them. Sunken drifts around the hay yard were a reminder of how many times the boys had had to shovel out there to keep the calves from walking into the stacks across the top of them. Across the wan and disheveled yard the willows were bare, and beyond them the flood-plain hill was brown. The sky was roiled with gray cloud.

Matted, filthy, lifeless, littered, the place of her winter imprisonment was exposed, ugly enough to put gooseflesh up her backbone, and with the carrion smell over all of it. It was like a bad and disgusting wound, infected wire cut or proud flesh or the gangrene of frostbite, with the bandage off. With her packed trunk and her telescope bag and two loaded grain sacks behind her, she stood in the door waiting for Ray to come with the buckboard, and she was sick to be gone.

Yet when he did come, with the boys all slopping through the mud behind him, and they threw her trunk and telescope and bags into the buckboard and tied the tarp down and there was nothing left to do but go, she faced them with a sudden, desolating desire to cry. She laughed, and caught her lower lip under her teeth and bit down hard on it, and went around to shake one hoof-like hand after the other, staring into each face in turn and seeing in each something that made it all the harder to say something easy: Goodbye. Red-bearded, black-bearded, gray-bristled, clean-shaven (for her?), two of them with puckered sunken scars on the cheekbones, all of them seedy, matted-haired, weathered and cracked as old lumber left out for years, they looked sheepish, or sober, or cheerful, and said things like, "Well, Molly, have you a nice trip, now," or "See you in Malta maybe." They had been her family. She had looked after them, fed them, patched their clothes, unraveled old socks to knit them new ones, cut their hair, lanced their boils, tended their wounds. Now it was like the gathered-in family parting at the graveside after someone's funeral.

She had begun quite openly to cry. She pulled her cheeks down, opened her mouth, dabbed at her eyes with her knuckles, laughed. "Now you all take care," she said. "And come see us, you hear? Jesse? Rusty? Slip? Buck, when you come I'll fix you a better patch on your pants than that one. Goodbye, Panguingue, you were the best man I had on the coal scuttle. Don't you forget me. Little Horn, I'm *sorry* we ran out of pie fixings. When you come to Malta I'll make you a peach pie a yard across."

She could not have helped speaking their names, as if to name them were to insure their permanence. But she knew that though she might see them, or most of them, when Ray brought the drive in to Malta in July, these were friends who would soon be lost for good. They had already got the word: sweep the range and sell everything — steers, bulls, calves, cows — for whatever it would bring. Put a For Sale sign on the ranch, or simply abandon it. The country had rubbed its lesson in. Like half the outfits between the Milk and the CPR, the T-Down was quitting. As for her, she was quitting first.

She saw Ray slumping, glooming down from the buckboard seat with the reins wrapped around one gloved hand. Dude and Dinger were hipshot in the harness. As Rusty and Little Horn gave Molly a hand up to climb the wheel, Dude raised his tail and dropped an oaty bundle of dung on the singletree, but she did not even bother to make a face or say something provoked and joking. She was watching Ray, looking right into his grey eyes and his somber dark face and seeing all at once what the winter of disaster had done to him. His cheek, like Ed's and Rusty's, was puckered with frost scars; frost had nibbled at the lobes of his ears; she could see the strain of bone-cracking labor, the bitterness of failure, in the lines from his nose to the corners of his mouth. Making room for her, he did not smile. With her back momentarily to the others, speaking only for him, she said through her tight teeth, "Let's git!"

Promptly — he was always prompt and ready — he plucked whip from whipsocket. The tip snapped on Dinger's haunch, the lurch of the buggy threw her so that she could cling and not have to turn to reveal her face. "Goodbye!" she cried, more into the collar of her mackinaw than to them, throwing the words over her shoulder like a flower or a coin, and tossed her left hand in the air and shook it. The single burst of their voices chopped off into silence. She heard only the grate of the tires in gravel; beside her the wheel poured yellow drip. She concentrated on it, fighting her lips that wanted to blubber.

"This could be bad for a minute," Ray said. She looked up. Obediently she clamped thumb and finger over her nose. To their right, filling half of Frying Pan Flat, was the boneyard, two acres of carcasses scattered where the boys had dragged them after skinning them out when they found them dead in the brush. It did not seem that off there they could smell, for the chinook was blowing out in light airs from the west. But when she let go her nose she smelled it rich and rotten, as if it rolled upwind the way water runs upstream in an eddy.

Beside her Ray was silent. The horses were trotting now in the soft sand of the patrol trail. On both sides the willows were gnawed down to stubs, broken and mouthed and gummed off by starving cattle. There was floodwater in the low spots, and the sound of running water under the drifts of every side coulee.

Once Ray said, ''Harry Willis says a railroad survey's coming right up the Whitemud valley this summer. S'pose that'll mean homesteaders in here, maybe a town.''

''I s'pose.''

''Make it a little easier when you run out of prunes, if there was a store at Whitemud.''

''Well,'' she said, ''we won't be here to run out,'' and then immediately, as she caught a whiff that gagged her, ''Pee-you! Hurry up!''

Ray did not touch up the team. ''What for?'' he said. ''To get to the next one quicker?''

She appraised the surliness of his voice, and judged that some of it was general disgust and some of it was aimed at her. But what did he want? Every time she made a suggestion of some outfit around Malta or Chinook where he might get a job he humped his back and looked impenetrable. What *did* he want? To come back here and take another licking? When there wasn't even a cattle outfit left, except maybe the little ones like the Z-X and the Lazy-S? And where one winter could kill you, as it had just killed the T-Down? She felt like yelling at him, ''Look at your face. Look at your hands — you can't open them even halfway, for calluses. For what? Maybe three thousand cattle left out of ten thousand, and them skin and bone. Why wouldn't I be glad to get out? Who *cares* if there's a store at Whitemud? You're just like an old bulldog with his teeth clinched in somebody's behind, and it'll take a pry-bar to make you unclinch!'' She said nothing; she forced herself to breathe evenly the tainted air.

Floodwater forced them out of the bottoms and up onto the second floodplain. Below them Molly saw the river astonishingly wide, pushing across willow bars and pressing deep into the cutbank bends. She could hear it, when the wheels went quietly — a hushed roar like wind. Cattle were balloonily afloat in the brush where they had died. She saw a brindle longhorn waltz around the deep water of a bend with his legs in the air, and farther on a whiteface that stranded momentarily among flooded rosebushes, and rotated free, and stranded again.

Their bench was cut by a side coulee, and they tipped and rocked down, the rumps of the horses back against the dashboard, Ray's hand on the brake, the shoes screeching mud from the tires. There was brush in the bottom, and stained drifts still unmelted. Their wheels sank in slush, she hung to the seat rail, they righted, the lines cracked across the muscling rumps as the team dug in and lifted them out of the cold, snowbank breath of the draw. Then abruptly, in a hollow on the right, dead eyeballs stared at her from between spraddled legs, horns and tails and legs were tangled in a starved mass of bone and hide not yet, in that cold bottom, puffing with the gases of decay. They must have been three deep — piled on one another, she supposed, while drifting before some one of the winter's blizzards.

A little later, accosted by a stench so overpowering that she breathed it in deeply as if to sample the worst, she looked to the left and saw a longhorn, its belly blown up ready to pop, hanging by neck and horns from a tight clump of alder and black birch where the snow had left him. She saw the wind make catspaws in the heavy winter hair.

"O God!" Ray said, "when you find 'em in *trees*!"

His boots, worn and whitened by many wettings, were braced against the dash. From the corner of her eye Molly could see his glove, its wrist-lace open. His wrist looked as wide as a doubletree, the sleeve of his Levi jacket was tight with forearm. The very sight of his strength made her hate the tone of defeat and outrage in his voice. Yet she appraised the tone cunningly, for she did not want him somehow butting his bullheaded way back into it. There were better things they could do than break their backs and hearts in a hopeless country a hundred miles from anywhere.

With narrowed eyes, caught in an instant vision, she saw the lilac bushes by the front porch of her father's house, heard the screen door bang behind her brother Charley (screen doors!), saw people passing, women in dresses, maybe all going to a picnic or a ballgame down in the park by the river. She passed the front of McCabe's General Store and through the window saw the counters and shelves: dried apples, dried peaches, prunes, tapioca, Karo syrup, everything they had done without for six weeks; and new white-stitched overalls, yellow horsehide gloves, varnished axe handles, barrels of flour and bags of sugar, shiny boots and workshoes, counters full of calico and flowered voile and crepe de chine and curtain net, whole stacks of flypaper stuck sheet to sheet, jars of peppermints and striped candy and horehound . . . She giggled.

"What?" Ray's neck and shoulders were so stiff with muscle that he all but creaked when he turned his head.

"I was just thinking. Remember the night I used our last sugar to make that batch of divinity, and dragged all the boys in after bedtime to eat it?"

"Kind of saved the day," Ray said. "Took the edge off ever'body."

"Kind of left us starving for sugar, too. I can still see them picking up those little bitty dabs of fluff with their fingers like tongs, and stuffing them in among their whiskers and making faces, *yum yum,* and wondering what on earth had got into me."

"Nothing got into you. You was just fed up. We all was."

"Remember when Slip picked up that pincushion I was tatting a cover for, and I got sort of hysterical and asked him if he knew what it was? Remember what he said? 'It a doll piller, ain't it, Molly?' I thought I'd die."

She shook her head angrily. Ray was looking sideward at

her in alarm. She turned her face away and stared down across the water that spread nearly a half-mile wide in the bottoms. Dirty foam and brush circled in the eddies. She saw a slab cave from an almost drowned cutbank and sink bubbling. From where they drove, between the water and the outer slope that rolled up to the high prairie, the Cypress Hills made a snow-patched, tree-darkened dome across the west. The wind came off them mild as milk. Poisoned! she told herself, and dragged it deep into her lungs.

She was aware again of Ray's gray eye. "Hard on you," he said. For some reason he made her mad, as if he were accusing her of bellyaching. She felt how all the time they bumped and rolled along the shoulder of the river valley they had this antagonism between them like a snarl of barbed wire. You couldn't reach out anywhere without running into it. Did he blame her for going home, or what? What did he expect her to do, come along with a whole bunch of men on that roundup, spend six or eight weeks in pants out among the carcasses? And then what?

A high, sharp whicker came downwind. The team chuckled and surged into their collars. Looking ahead, she saw a horse — picketed or hobbled — and a man who leaned on something — rifle? — watching them. "Young Schulz," Ray said, and then here came the dogs, four big bony hounds. The team began to dance. Ray held them in tight and whistled the buggywhip in the air when the hounds got too close.

Young Schulz, Molly saw as they got closer, was leaning on a shovel, not a rifle. He had dug a trench two or three feet deep and ten or twelve long. He dragged a bare forearm across his forehead under a muskrat cap: a sullen-faced boy with eyes like dirty ice. She supposed he had been living all alone since his father had disappeared. Somehow he made her want to turn her lips inside out. A wild man. She had not liked his father and she did not like him.

The hounds below her were sniffing at the wheels and

testing the air up in her direction, wagging slow tails. "What've you got, wolves?" Ray asked.

"Coyotes."

"Old ones down there?"

"One, anyway. Chased her in."

"Find any escape holes?"

"One. Plugged it."

"You get 'em the hard way," Ray said. "How've you been doing on wolves?"

The boy said a hard four-letter word, slanted his eyes sideward at Molly in something less than apology — acknowledgement, maybe. "The dogs ain't worth a damn without Puma to kill for 'em. Since he got killed they just catch up with a wolf and run alongside him. I dug out a couple dens."

With his thumb and finger he worked at a pimple under his jaw. The soft wind blew over them, the taint of carrion only a suspicion, perhaps imaginary. The roily sky had begun to break up in patches of blue. Beside her Molly felt the solid bump of Ray's shoulder as he twisted to cast a weather eye upward. "Going to be a real spring day," he said. To young Schulz he said, "How far in that burrow go, d'you s'pose?"

"Wouldn't ordinarily go more'n twenty feet or so."

"Need any help diggin'?"

The Schulz boy spat. "Never turn it down."

"Ray . . ." Molly said. But she stopped when she saw his face.

"Been a long time since I helped dig out a coyote," he said. He watched her as if waiting for a reaction. "Been a long time since I did anything for *fun*."

"Oh, go ahead!" she said. "Long as we don't miss that train."

"I guess we can make Maple Creek by noon tomorrow. And you ain't in such a hurry you have to be there sooner, are you?"

She had never heard so much edge in his voice. He looked at her as if he hated her. She turned so as to keep the Schulz boy from seeing her face, and for just a second she and Ray were all alone up there, eye to eye. She laid a hand on his knee. "I don't know what it is," she said. "Honestly I don't. But you better work it off."

Young Schulz went back to his digging while Ray unhitched and looped the tugs and tied the horses to the wheels. Then Ray took the shovel and began to fill the air with clods. He moved more dirt than the Fresno scrapers she had seen grading the railroad back home; he worked as if exercising his muscles after a long layoff, as if spring had fired him up and set him to running. The soil was sandy and came out in clean brown shovelfuls. The hounds lay back out of range and watched. Ray did not look toward Molly, or say anything to Schulz. He just moved dirt as if dirt was his worst enemy. After a few minutes Molly pulled the buffalo robe out of the buckboard and spread it on the drying prairie. By that time it was getting close to noon. The sun was full out; she felt it warm on her face and hands.

The coyote hole ran along about three feet underground. From where she sat she could look right up the trench, and see the black opening at the bottom when the shovel broke into it. She could imagine the coyotes crammed back at the end of their burrow, hearing the noises and seeing the growing light as their death dug toward them, and no way out, nothing to do but wait.

Young Schulz took the shovel and Ray stood out of the trench, blowing. The violent work seemed to have made him more cheerful. He said to Schulz, when the boy stooped and reached a gloved hand up the hole, "She comes out of there in a hurry she'll run right up your sleeve."

Schulz grunted and resumed his digging. The untroubled sun went over, hanging almost overhead, and an untroubled wind stirred the old grass. Over where the last terrace of the flood-plain rolled up to the prairie the first gopher of the season sat up and looked them over. A dog moved, and he disappeared with a flirt of his tail. Ray was rolling up his sleeves, whistling loosely between his teeth. His forearms were white, his hands blackened and cracked as the charred ends of sticks. His eyes touched her — speculatively, she thought. She smiled, making a forgiving, kissing motion of her mouth, but all he did in reply was work his eyebrows, and she could not tell what he was thinking.

Young Schulz was poking up the hole with the shovel handle. Crouching in the trench in his muskrat cap, he looked like some digging animal; she half expected him to put his nose into the hole and sniff and then start throwing dirt out between his hind legs.

Then in a single convulsion of movement Schulz rolled sideward. A naked-gummed thing of teeth and gray fur shot into sight, scrambled at the edge, and disappeared in a pinwheel of dogs. Molly leaped to the heads of the horses, rearing and wall-eyed and yanking the light buckboard sideways, and with a hand in each bridle steadied them down. Schulz, she saw, was circling the dogs with the shotgun, but the dogs had already done it for him. The roaring and snapping tailed off. Schulz kicked the dogs away and with one quick flash and circle and rip tore the scalp and ears off the coyote. It lay there wet, mauled, bloody, with its pink skull bare — a little dog brutally murdered. One of the hounds came up, sniffed with its neck stretched out, sank its teeth in the coyote's shoulder, dragged it a foot or two.

"Ray . . ." Molly said.

He did not hear her; he was blocking the burrow with the shovel blade while Schulz went over to his horse. The boy came back with a red willow stick seven or eight feet long, forked like a small slingshot at the end. Ray pulled away the shovel and Schulz twisted in the hole with the forked end of the stick. A hard grunt came out of him, and he backed up, pulling the stick from the hole. At the last moment he yanked hard, and a squirm of gray broke free and rolled and was pounced on by the hounds.

This time Ray kicked them aside. He picked up the pup by

the tail, and it hung down and kicked its hind legs a little. Schulz was down again, probing the burrow, twisting, probing again, twisting hard.

Again he backed up, working the entangled pup out carefully until it was in the open, and then landing it over his head like a sucker from the river. The pup landed within three feet of the buckboard wheel, and floundered, stunned. In an instant Molly dropped down and smothered it in clothes, hands, arms. There was snarling in her very ear, she was bumped hard, she heard Ray yelling, and then he had her on her feet. From his face, she thought he was going to hit her. Against her middle, held by the scruff and grappled with the other arm, the pup snapped and slavered with needle teeth. She felt the sting of bites on her hands and wrists. The dogs ringed her, ready to jump, kept off by Ray's kicking boot.

"God a'mighty," Ray said, "you want to get yourself killed?"

"I didn't want the dogs to get him."

"No. What are you going to do with him? We'll just have to knock him in the head."

"I'm going to keep him."

"In Malta?"

"Why not?"

He let go his clutch on her arm. "He'll be a cute pup for a month and then he'll be a chicken thief and then somebody'll shoot him."

"At least he'll have a little bit of life. Get *away,* you dirty, murdering . . . !" She cradled the thudding little body along one arm under her mackinaw, keeping her hold in the scruff with her right hand, and turned herself away from the crowding hounds. "I'm going to tame him," she said. "I don't care what you say."

"Scalp's worth three dollars," Schulz said from the edge of the ditch.

Ray kicked the dogs back. His eyes, ordinarily so cool and

gray, looked hot. The digging and the excitement did not seem to have taken the edge off whatever was eating him. He said, "Look, maybe you have to go back home to your folks, but you don't have to take a menagerie along. What are you going to do with him on the train?"

But now it was out. He did blame her. "You think I'm running out on you," she said.

"I just said you can't take a menagerie back to town."

"You said *maybe* I had to go home. Where else would I go? You're going to be on roundup till July. The ranch is going to be sold. Where on earth *would* I go but home?"

"You don't have to stay. You don't have to make me go back to ridin' for some outfit for twenty a month and found."

His dark, battered, scarred face told her to be quiet. Dipping far down in the tight pocket of his Levis he brought up his snap purse and took from it three silver dollars. Young Schulz, who had been probing the den to see if anything else was there, climbed out of the ditch and took the money in his dirty chapped hand. He gave Molly one cool look with his dirty-ice eyes, scalped the dead pup, picked up shotgun and twisting-stick and shovel, tied them behind the saddle, mounted, whistled at the dogs, and with barely a nod rode off toward the northeastern flank of the Hills. The hounds fanned out ahead of him, running loose and easy. In the silence their departure left behind, a clod broke and rolled into the ditch. A gopher piped somewhere. The wind moved quiet as breathing in the grass.

Molly drew a breath that caught a little — a sigh for their quarreling, for whatever bothered him so deeply that he gloomed and grumped and asked something impossible of her — but when she spoke she spoke around it. "No thanks for your digging."

"He don't know much about living with people."

"He's like everything else in this country, wild and dirty and thankless."

In a minute she would really start feeling sorry for herself.

But why not? Did it ever occur to him that since November, when they came across the prairie on their honeymoon in this same buckboard, she had seen exactly one woman, for one day and a night? Did he have any idea how she had felt, a bride of three weeks, when he went out with the boys on late fall roundup and was gone ten days, through three different blizzards, while she stayed home and didn't know whether he was dead or alive?

"If you mean me," Ray said, "I may be wild and I'm probably dirty, but I ain't thankless, honey." Shamed, she opened her mouth to reply, but he was already turning away to rummage up a strap and a piece of whang leather to make a collar and leash for her pup.

"Are you hungry?" she said to his shoulders.

"Any time."

"I put up some sandwiches."

"O.K."

"Oh, Ray," she said, "let's not crab at each other! Sure I'm glad we're getting out. Is that so awful? I hate to see you killing yourself bucking this *hopeless* country. But does that mean we have to fight? I thought maybe we could have a picnic like we had coming in, back on that slough where the ducks kept coming in and landing on the ice and skidding end over end. I don't know, it don't hardly seem we've laughed since."

"Well," he said, "it ain't been much of a laughing winter, for a fact." He had cut down a cheekstrap and tied a rawhide thong on it. Carefully she brought out the pup and he buckled the collar around its neck, but when she set it on the ground it backed up to the end of the thong, cringing and showing its naked gums, so that she picked it up again and let it dig along her arm, hunting darkness under her mackinaw.

"Shall we eat here?" Ray said. "Kind of a lot of chewed-up coyote around."

"Let's go up on the bench."

"Want to tie the pup in the buckboard?"

"I'll take him. I want to get him used to me."

"O.K.," he said. "You go on. I'll tie a nosebag on these nags and bring the robe and the lunchbox."

She walked slowly, not to scare the pup, until she was up the little bench and onto the prairie. From up there she could see not only the Cypress Hills across the west, but the valley of the Whitemud breaking out of them, and a big slough, spread by floodwater, and watercourses going both ways out of it, marked by thin willows. Just where the Whitemud emerged from the hills were three white dots — the Mountie post, probably, or the Lazy-S, or both. The sun was surprisingly warm, until she counted up and found that it was May 8. It ought to be warm.

Ray brought the buffalo robe and spread it, and he sat down. One-handed because she had the thong of the leash wrapped around her palm, she doled out sandwiches and hard-boiled eggs. Ray popped a whole egg in his mouth, and chewing, pointed. "There goes the South Fork of the Swift Current, out of the slough. The one this side, that little scraggle of willows you can see, empties into the Whitemud. That slough sits right on the divide and runs both ways. You don't see that very often."

She appraised his tone. He was feeling better. For that matter, so was she. It had turned out a beautiful day, with big fair-weather clouds coasting over. She saw the flooded river bottoms below them, on the left, darken to winter and then sweep bright back to spring again while she could have counted no more than ten. As she moved, the coyote pup clawed and scrambled against her side, and she said, wrinkling her nose in her Freckleface smile, "If he started eating me, I wonder if I could keep from yelling? Did you ever read the story about the boy that hid the fox under his clothes and the fox started eating a hole in him and the boy never batted an eye, just let himself be chewed?"

"No, I never heard that one," Ray said. "Don't seem very likely, does it?" He lay back and turned his face, shut-eyed, into the sun. Now and then his hand rose to feed bites of sandwich into his mouth.

''The pup's quieter,'' Molly said. ''I bet he'll tame. I wonder if he'd eat a piece of sandwich?''

''Leave him be for a while, I would.''

''I guess.''

His hand reached over blindly and she put another sandwich into its pincer claws. Chewing, he came up on an elbow; his eyes opened, he stared a long time down into the flooded bottoms and then across toward the slough and the hills. ''Soon as the sun comes out, she don't look like the same country, does she?''

Molly said nothing. She watched his nostrils fan in and out as he sniffed. ''No smell up here, do you think?'' he said. But she heard the direction he was groping in, the regret that could lead, if they did not watch out, to some renewed and futile hope, and she said tartly, ''I can smell it, all right.''

He sighed. He lay back and closed his eyes. After about three minutes he said, ''Boy, what a day, though. I won't get through on the patrol trail goin' back. The ice'll be breakin' up before tonight, at this rate. Did you hear it crackin' and poppin' a minute ago?''

''I didn't hear it.''

''Listen.''

They were still. She heard the soft wind move in the prairie wool, and beyond it, filling the background, the hushed and hollow noise of the floodwater, sigh of drowned willows, suck of whirlpools, splash and gurgle as cutbanks caved, and the steady push and swash and ripple of moving water. Into the soft rush of sound came a muffled report like a tree cracking, or a shot a long way off. ''Is that it?'' she said. ''Is that the ice letting loose?''

''Stick around till tomorrow and you'll see that whole channel full of ice.''

Another shadow from one of the big flat-bottomed clouds chilled across them and passed. Ray said into the air, ''Harry

Willis said this railroad survey will go right through to Medicine Hat. Open up this whole country."

Now she sat very still, stroking the soft bulge of the pup through the cloth.

"Probably mean a town at Whitemud."

"You told me."

"With a store that close we couldn't get quite so snowed in as we did this winter."

Molly said nothing, because she dared not. They were a couple that, like the slough spread out northwest of them, flowed two ways, he to this wild range, she back to town and friends and family. And yet in the thaw of one bright day, their last together up here north of the Line, she teetered. She feared the softening that could start her draining toward his side.

"Molly," Ray said, and made her look at him. She saw him as the country and the winter had left him, weathered and scarred. His eyes were gray and steady, marksman's eyes.

She made a wordless sound that sounded in her own ears almost a groan. "You want awful bad to stay," she said.

His tong fingers plucked a strand of grass, he bit it between his teeth, his head went slowly up and down.

"But how?" she said. "Do you want to strike the Z-X for a job, or the Lazy-S, or somebody? Do you want to open a store in Whitemud for when the railroad comes through, or what?"

"Haven't you figured that out yet?" he said. "Kept waitin' for you to see it. I want to buy the T-Down."

"You *what*?"

"I want us to buy the T-Down and make her go."

She felt that she went all to pieces. She laughed. She threw her hands around so that the pup scrambled and clawed at her side. "Ray Henry," she said, "you're crazy as a bedbug. Even if it made any sense, which it doesn't, where'd we get the money?"

"Borrow it."

"Go in debt to stay up *here*?"

"Molly," he said, and she heard the slow gather of

determination in his voice, "when else could we pick up cattle for twenty dollars a head with sucking calves thrown in? When else could we get a whole ranch layout for a few hundred bucks? That Goodnight herd we were running was the best herd in Canada, maybe anywhere. This spring roundup we could take our pick of what's left, including bulls, and put our brand on 'em and turn 'em into summer range and drive everything else to Malta. We wouldn't want more than three-four hundred head. We can swing that much, and we can cut enough hay to bring that many through even a winter like this last one."

She watched him; her eyes groped and slipped. He said, "We're never goin' to have another chance like this as long as we live. This country's goin' to change; there'll be homesteaders in here soon as the railroad comes. Towns, stores, what you've been missin'. Women folks. And we can sit out here on the Whitemud with good hay land and good range and just make this goldarned country holler uncle."

"How long?" she said. "How long have you been thinking this way?"

"Since we got John's letter."

"You never said anything."

"I kept waitin' for you to get the idea yourself. But you were hell bent to get out."

She escaped his eyes, looked down, shifted carefully to accommodate the wild thing snuggled in darkness at her waist, and as she moved, her foot scuffed up the scalloped felt edge of the buffalo robe. By her toe was a half-crushed crocus, palely lavender, a thing so tender and unbelievable in the waste of brown grass under the great pour of sky that she cried out, "Why, good land, look at that!" — taking advantage of it both as discovery and as diversion.

"Crocus?" Ray said, bending. "Don't take long, once the snow goes."

It lay in her palm, a thing lucky as a four-leaf clover, and as if it had had some effect in clearing her sight, Molly looked down the south-facing slope and saw it tinged with faintest green. She put the crocus to her nose, but smelled only a mild freshness, an odor no more showy than of grass. But maybe enough to cover the scent of carrion.

Her eyes came up and found Ray's watching her steadily. "You think we could do it," she said.

"I know we could."

"It's a funny time to start talking that way, when I'm on my way out."

"You don't have to stay out."

Sniffing the crocus, she put her right hand under the mackinaw until her fingers touched fur. The pup stiffened but did not turn or snap. She moved her fingers softly along his back, willing him tame. For some reason she felt as if she might burst out crying.

"Haven't you got any ambition to be the first white woman in five hundred miles?" Ray said.

Past and below him, three or four miles off, she saw the great slough darken under a driving cloud shadow and then brighten to a blue that danced with little wind-whipped waves. She wondered what happened to the ice in a slough like that, whether it went on down the little flooded creeks to add to the jams in the Whitemud and Swift Current, or whether it just rose to the surfacc and gradually melted there. She didn't suppose it would be spectacular like the break-up in the river.

"Mumma and Dad would think we'd lost our minds," she said. "How much would we have to borrow?"

"Maybe six or eight thousand."

"Oh Lord!" She contemplated the sum, a burden of debt heavy enough to pin them down for life. She remembered the winter, six months of unremitting slavery and imprisonment. She lifted the crocus and laid it against Ray's dark scarred cheek.

"You should never wear lavender," she said, and giggled at the very idea, and let her eyes come up to his and stared at him, sick and scared. "All right," she said. "If it's what you want."

LAND
Fort Walsh
THE
LEADER
COMPANY
LIMITED

CAPE

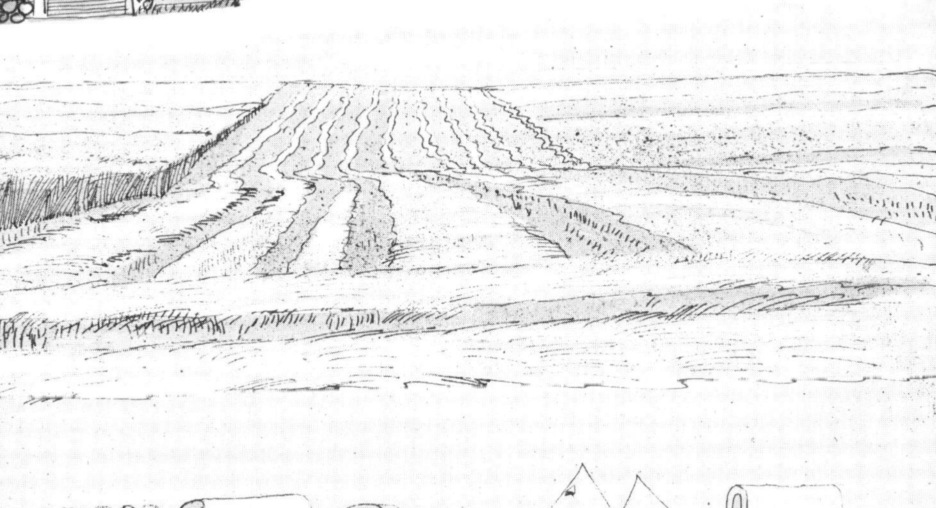

James P. McLachlan

And My Heart Soars

Chief Dan George

The beauty of the trees,
the softness of the air,
the fragrance of the grass,
    speaks to me.

The summit of the mountain,
the thunder of the sky,
the rhythm of the sea,
    speaks to me.

The faintness of the stars,
the freshness of the morning,
the dew drop on the flower,
    speaks to me.

The strength of fire,
the taste of salmon,
the trail of the sun,
And the life that never goes away,
    They speak to me.

And my heart soars.

Berry-Picking

James M. Moir

Submerged in a foam of leaves
we take from the river of summer
its purple treasure.

The sun pours burning gold
into the valley;

And a crow, deep among trees,
gives the peculiar drowsy call
of mid-July.

On the rim far beyond us
horses, free of the saddle,
stand in the lazy wind.

We alone have cast off langour;
to-day we gather
summer in our buckets;

for a quick foreboding of winter
shows a jar of fruit in a window
that reflects a diminished sun.

Saskatchewan

Edward A. McCourt

Saskatchewan's welcome to the tourist is reserved, unenthusiastic. Not even a service station marks the point of entry, only a modest roadside sign informing us that we are now in the Wheat Province.

The Highway is excellent, the country dull — a combination that tempts even the most conservative and law-abiding among us to press the gas-pedal to the floor. But no matter how high the speedometer climbs we must yield sooner or later to a sense of utter frustration. For nothing changes. Not the land unrolling like wrinkled parchment on either side of the Highway to a point beyond the range of sight (or so it seems, for a blue haze shrouds the horizon); and not the enormous bowl of sky through which a jet traces a visible line 300 miles long. The Highway curves from time to time for no apparent reason, except, perhaps, to counteract road hypnosis, and no surprises lie in wait around the next bend.

Or the next.

Empty land. Empty sky. A stranger to the prairies feels uneasily that he is driving straight into infinity.

The land is without character. It excites neither hatred nor love. There is nothing here to respond to. Not the austere, sinister loneliness of a true desert nor the friendly security of a conventional pastoral landscape. Seen from the Highway, south-eastern Saskatchewan is scruffy rather than desolate. It rolls not in great swells but choppily, in hillocks and ridges a few feet high; it is trenched by shallow gullies and dotted by tufts of woodland — poplar and willow mostly — which, because they form no consistent pattern in the landscape, create a curious effect of ill-grooming. Here and there a slough (a body of stagnant water) provides a welcome break in the monotony. In sunlight it is an eye-dazzling, sky-reflected blue, at twilight a black miasmal tarn. Many prosperous farm homes are visible from the Highway, crouched secure behind squat caragana hedges and towering evergreen windbreaks. But the deserted farmsteads make the greater impact; they offend the eye and depress the soul. The weather-blackened, two-storey houses with vacant, eye-like windows are reminiscent to a reader of Edgar Allen Poe of the gloom-ridden House of Usher. And, one suspects, many a farm wife of a past generation must have felt a strong sense of kinship with the tragic Lady Madeline: the kinship of being buried alive.

The sense of depression is unjustified; the deserted farms are no symbols of the triumph of hostile nature over man. The land is rich and well-cultivated; given the needed moisture — and its demands are modest — it will produce forty bushels to the acre of the world's finest wheat. But farming in Saskatchewan and generally throughout the West is fast becoming big business. The homesteader who half a century ago reared a family on 160 acres is gone now and his children scattered the length and breadth of the land. The deserted farmsteads are reminders of a vanished, not vanquished, generation. The farms on which barns and houses are crumbling to ruins are probably units of a single enterprise that may encompass thousands of acres. If a marine metaphor may be applied to an almost waterless land: the big fish have swallowed the little and grown bigger. And as likely as not the big fish lives in town and commutes to the farm.

Not even the extension to rural communities of such utilities as light and power and indoor plumbing has checked appreciably the drift from farm to town. Saskatchewan is a land in which modern man finds it hard to live with and by himself. Especially at night when the loneliness closes in and earth and sky assume a detachment and an immensity that compel an awareness of worlds not realized in the light of common day.

Moosomin is the first town of consequence inside the Saskatchewan border. It is a decent, sober place filled with decent, sober people, some of whom live in brick houses — a comparative rarity in Saskatchewan — reminiscent to the Easterner of home. In 1885 Moosomin, although several hundred miles from the battlefields, played a minor supporting role in the drama of the Riel Rebellion. The firebrand Major Boulton, hell-bent to avenge his imprisonment under Riel in Fort Garry fifteen years before, outfitted a troop of volunteers in the town, and after the rebellion was over, returned to disband the troop and sell their equipment back to the townsfolk. But since 1885 nothing much has happened in Moosomin to attract the attention of historian or folklorist.

It would be wrong, though, to assume that the history of south-eastern Saskatchewan was generally as uninteresting as its landscape. The town of Whitewood, twenty miles along the Highway from Moosomin, is today indistinguishable in appearance and activities from nearly every other town of comparable size in the West; but eighty years ago it boasted a community organization unique in the annals of musicology and pioneer culture — a brass band led by an Oxford Classics M.A. (the local schoolmaster) and numbering in its ranks no fewer than four authentic French counts. It is natural to hope that at least one of these blue bloods played the French horn, but tradition insists that they all favoured the tuba.

In the eighties and nineties the counts cut a wide social and economic swath in the south-eastern corner of Saskatchewan. Haters of French republicanism and victims of heavy taxation, they no doubt hoped to recoup their fortunes in the New World and over their cups plot the restoration of the Bourbons to the throne of France. They were enterprising men of soaring imagination; they had some capital of their own and access to more, and they were spenders on a grand scale. The prairies defeated them in the end and sent them back to France, but during their brief hour of glory they and their lively wives dominated the social life of Whitewood and brought to the community a Gallic elegance and grace which won the astonished admiration and eventually the affection of even their extremist republican neighbours.

Comte de Jumilhac ran a sheep-ranch on the banks of the Pipestone Creek ten miles south of town. He was the biggest and loudest cornct-and-tuba player in the band, and numbered a great Cardinal among his ancestors. He died in his native land as the Marquis de Richelieu. ("Nothing wobbly about the counts," said one who knew them well. "They were of ancient, some of royal lineage.") Comte de Langle raised fine race-horses which he always sold at a loss; Baron de Brabant grew and canned chicory which no one in the West would buy at any price. Monsieur Janet assisted by Comte de Seysells established a cheese factory and produced what he called a Gruyere cheese. He was the first to admit that it was inedible. Comte de Roffignac promoted a vast sugar-beet enterprise which excited the imagination of half Western Canada and failed through lack of funds and moisture. Comte de Beaulincourt lived in the middle of a poplar bluff on the outskirts of the town and painted landscapes in oils. None of his paintings appears to have survived.

As businessmen, the counts were magnificent failures, but for a decade or more their social supremacy was unquestioned. They brought with them retinues of servants from France, they imported the best of foods and wines, and they drove over rutted trails in costumes and equipage — tall hats, white gloves, dog-carts, coaches — unlike anything seen on the prairie before or since. One year they took over the Commercial Hotel in Whitewood and gave a party that is still talked about by the descendants of the guests. "The Frenchmen invited the elite of the district and some who were not so elite or anything else," runs an eyewitness report. "It was a grand success. One would not have thought it possible to scare up so many claw-hammer coats and white shirts and low-necked dresses in the whole country. But they were there. And the French counts were certainly good and gracious hosts."

Their courtesy was instinctive and without limits. During the First World War the Whitewood blacksmith went overseas with a Canadian battalion, and when on leave in France called on Comte Henri de Soras, then living out his last years in his native land. To his dismay the blacksmith found the count living in a "noble ancestral mansion". But he was received literally and figuratively with open arms, and his leave terminated with a formal dinner in his honour "to which all the French noblesse of the district were invited." The blacksmith, far from being embarrassed, had the time of his life. So, one suspects, did the count.

"The gallant and courteous gentlemen of Old France," as one crusty republican old timer called them without irony, have long since been gathered to their fathers, but their memory still lingers in the Whitewood district like an exotic and gracious fragrance. The tourist who has an hour or two to spare is well advised to leave the Highway and drive south from the town for ten miles into the lovely, gentle valley of the Pipestone Creek. For the valley was the peculiar preserve of the counts, and no one can deny them an eye for beauty. Their houses, amply built on admirable vantage-points overlooking the valley, have like their builders long since disappeared; but near the rim of the valley the Mission of St. Hubert's stands as concrete evidence of the devotion of the counts to the ancient faith (they built the original Mission church), and the valley itself is unchanged. The tourist who enjoys the primitive life should camp for a night beside the Pipestone Creek. For if the moon is right and his ear properly attuned he may hear, through the yelping of coyotes on some far-off hill-side and the hum of mosquitoes close at hand, the notes of a ghostly tuba echoing between the valley walls.

Between Whitewood and Indian Head, sixty-five miles farther west, there is little variation in the pattern of earth and sky. The towns and villages, each dominated by a row of monolithic elevators, slip past and none tempts the traveller to leave the Highway. Townsites were originally established along the CPR at eight- to twelve-mile intervals for the convenience of farmers who hauled their grain to the elevators over prairie trails by wagon or sleigh. But good roads and mechanized transport have wiped out the *raison d'etre* of half the villages of the West; they no longer serve any vital purpose and the wonder is that they contrive so tenaciously to exist.

Indian Head comes as a pleasant oasis to those who turn aside, for it is the centre of the first prairie Experimental Station (established 1888), and the gardens and trees of the town have benefited from the association. There are a few interesting old houses in Indian Head, survivors of the gingerbread and fretwork days, and the public buildings are handsome and well preserved.

Even those of us who, irrationally, love almost everything about Saskatchewan admit that the tourist won't be tempted to linger on the eastern stretch of the Highway. If he is travelling in midsummer the heat will be intense, and almost certainly he will find himself bucking a head-wind that blows with insistent, nerve-grating monotony from the west. Roadside tables are numerous but they offer dubious shelter from the blazing sun and buffeting wind, and most of the small-town motels seem appallingly exposed. Somewhere ahead lies the city of Regina where the usual tourist amenities — shower baths, air-conditioning, wall-to-wall broadloom, and cool dark taverns — are sure to be found, and the road to Regina runs wide and straight and marvellously uncluttered. But the wise tourist will eschew the temptations of the flesh; he will leave the Highway at Indian Head and drive north for twenty miles over Highway No. 56 into a region which seems no part of any familiar world, a region so vast, incongruous, and incomprehensible as to compel the exclamation, "It can't happen here."

Part of the fascination of the great valley of the Qu'Appelle lies in its total unexpectedness. I have driven into the valley many times, from the north and south, over paved highways, gravel roads, and dirt trails, and I have approached it on foot over naked, windswept prairie. Each time, the initial reaction has been the same — a mingling of awe and disbelief occasioned by what at first sight seems a fantastic mirage-in-reverse or a grand-scale hallucination. One moment, we are driving along an ordinary road through a typical south Saskatchewan landscape, level grain-fields on either side, no visible break in the terrain ahead; the next, we are hanging on the lip of a miniature Grand Canyon, in places more than two miles from rim to rim, lines defined with geometric precision, the floor of the valley as far as the eye can reach a necklace of sky blue lakes, each lake linked to the next by a sinuous slow moving river whose crazy convolutions persuade us that at times it doubles back on itself.

The valley of the Qu'Appelle cuts a great gash 250 miles long across the face of southern Saskatchewan. It extends from a point a few miles east of Elbow on the South Saskatchewan River to the junction of the Qu'Appelle and Assiniboine rivers just inside the Manitoba border. Like all prairie streams the Qu'Appelle is slow-flowing and turgid — no River of Life shown to the Evangelist, clear as crystal, babbling over rocks; but, to the traveller weary of the plains, the stream and the lakes and the valley are an authentic revelation.

As early as 1780 the ubiquitous Nor'Westers had established a trading post in the valley, and in the 1850s a Hudson's Bay post was built on the site of the present town of Fort Qu'Appelle (*not* to be confused with the town of Qu'Appelle on the Trans-Canada Highway). Indians and white trappers traded furs for pemmican at the post, and there such distinguished explorers and travellers as Palliser and the Earl of Southesk enjoyed the hospitality of the Great Company during their western journeyings. "The Qu'Appelle lakes may be considered the most western portion of the territory east of the Rocky Mountains into which the Hudson's Bay Company trade; westward of this is unknown, and the whole country untravelled by the white man." So Palliser reported, not altogether accurately, in 1858.

Following an influx of white settlers in the '70s and '80s, most of them from Eastern Canada and the Old Country, the town of Fort Qu'Appelle grew up around the Hudson's Bay post. Along the valley slopes the settlers built stone houses, some of which are still standing, and within the shelter of the great ramparts they lived lives considerably less harassed and wind blown than those of their fellows on the open prairie.

But life in the valley was not without its moments of drama. In 1881 Sitting Bull and his starving Sioux warriors, who had fled into Canada following the battle of the Little Big Horn and lived precariously ever since in the Cypress Hills and Moose Mountain districts, rode into the valley for a meeting with the North West Mounted Police under the command of Superintendent Sam Steele. The Sioux sought food, shelter, and a reservation; they wanted to become wards of the Canadian government. But international protocol forbade any such arrangement, and at last Sitting Bull, whose stoical dignity made a strong impression on all who met him, withdrew from the valley and rode back over the border to meet his death, several years later, at Wounded Knee.

In 1885 General Middleton moved from Qu'Appelle village into the valley to put the finishing touches on the training, such as it was, of his raw militia; and no doubt the boys from Winnipeg and the East had a fine time charging up and down the valley-slopes and shooting Indians who weren't there. They left the valley for the long march north — to near-disaster at Fish Creek and final victory at Batoche — when the willows were in bud and the gully streams in full spate. Among the units under Middleton's command was a volunteer force raised in the valley — dashing self-equipped Old Country men under the command of Captain John French, late of the Royal Ulster Militia. Old Middleton at once made it clear that he preferred the society of these "men of good family" to that of the raw colonials and thereby earned for himself and French's Scouts the lasting contempt of the Canadian troops. But the Scouts fought well enough; and Captain John French died at Batoche, shot through the head by a Metis sniper. He was buried in the Fort Qu'Appelle graveyard on the rim of the valley at a point overlooking the turquoise lakes linked by the meandering river. One suspects that if the dead could see he would have no interest in continuing his ascent to heaven.

Fort Qu'Appelle, built on the wide flats between Mission and Echo lakes, is a town on which age and history have conferred little dignity. The buildings are nondescript and the wind funnels eternally down the ragged, dusty main street, which seems about half a mile wide. But the valley-ramparts rise steeply just behind the town and the lakes stretch into the far distance. Whatever sins abide in the town itself are atoned for by the magnificence of its setting.

The Fort Hotel is worth a visit for its cuisine. In most Western small-town hotels and restaurants food is served to sustain life; in the Fort Hotel it also titillates the appetite. Over the door of the tap-room General Custer makes his Last Stand, courtesy of the Anheuser-Busch Brewing Company.

Five miles east of Fort Qu'Appelle on the shores of Mission Lake stands the village of Lebret, which has grown up around a Roman Catholic mission and an Indian residential school. The village is dominated by the elaborately decorated Mission Church of the Sacred Heart, built of local stone, and by the Fourteen Stations of the Cross straggling up the steep valley-slope to a tiny chapel near the top. The chapel is said to mark the site where, in 1860, the great western churchman Bishop Taché erected a cross and annexed the valley for Christ. Directly across the lake from the village a seminary nestles in the centre of a densely wooded stretch of valley. No visible trails lead to the seminary; in its isolation and serenity it takes us back centuries in time to that bright morning of the Christian church when godly men reared foundations of the faith in quiet wooded places and lived at peace with God and their fellows.

The visitor who has a little time to spend in the valley may choose his lodgings from among adequate motels, indifferent campsites, and a variety of rather primitively equipped rental cabins. Katepwa, a provincial park fourteen miles east of Fort Qu'Appelle on Highway 56, is a pinched, haphazard development, to be avoided on week-ends when it is unpleasantly crowded; and the lakes are usually better to look at than to swim in.

My first swim in Lake Katepwa was an experience which needs no nostalgic embroidering to make it brightly hued. My family and I had driven into the valley, which we had never before visited, on a scorching hot, dusty day over gravel and dirt roads. Ill-tempered and filthy, we took possession of the cabin we had rented sight unseen: an authentic museum-piece, lop-sided, leaky, weather-beaten, fronting a gravel-pit. "Haven't had time to get her really slicked up for you folks," the proprietor informed us with a genially villainous grin. "Eleven Montanans slept in her last night." So, we judged from the condition of the interior, did their horses. But no matter. A swim before supper in the cooling waters of the lake, a many-coloured jewel in the light of the setting sun, would make all things right. We had a race to see who got to the beach first. I won by several lengths and plunged in headlong. Then, before the horrified gaze of my wife and son, I rose from those cooling waters an ancient Briton come to life, from head to heel a dazzling indelible blue.

Algae forms in the lake-bottoms in the early summer; it rises and drifts about the surface with the wind. It contaminates beaches, kills fish and even livestock, turns unwary swimmers blue, and gives them the itch. In recent years government and cottagers have attempted to control the algae with a sulphate spray but it seems unlikely that the problem will be solved until the South Saskatchewan dam raises the water-level of the river and thus creates greater movement in the lake-bottoms. In the meantime, the wise visitor seeking exercise will content himself with a round of golf on the pleasant Fort Qu'Appelle course (where a slice on the eighth may land him in the cellar of the old Mounted Police post abandoned 1884), and a cool shower afterwards.

August is the busiest month in the valley. The farmers begin the harvest then, the Saskatchewan Arts Board conducts a variety of workshops in a group of made-over army huts on the fringes of Fort Qu'Appelle, and Indians from the prairie provinces and some of the adjoining states assemble for a pow-wow on the Pasqua Lake reserve a few miles west of the town. The Indians are readily distinguishable from the fine arts students — their costumes are more extensive and less brightly hued. At the pow-wow these pathetic descendants of the once-proud red man shuffle through the routines of their traditional dances within the shelter of a great circus tent and afterwards refresh themselves with spun candy and pop. The only visible drunks at the pow-wow are almost certain to be white spectators.

For the west-bound tourist the most convenient exit from the valley is by Highway No. 35, which joins the Trans-Canada Highway at the town of Qu'Appelle, twenty miles south of Fort Qu'Appelle. The town stands near the site of an early fur-trading post, and in 1885 it enjoyed an hour of national notoriety when General Middleton briefly established his headquarters in the hotel which still stands on the main street.

The forty mile run from Qu'Appelle to Regina again invites violation of the speed limit. In the distance the city skyscrapers loom far higher than they actually measure in storeys or feet — on the prairies anything taller than a grain elevator assumes the magnitude of a pyramid rising from desert sands. Viewed across miles of level, dusty plain a city skyline seems an incongruity and, to the stranger from a more sheltered environment, an immense reassurance.

And this, perhaps, is Regina's significant role. It offers the tourist the usual amenities to be expected in a city of 100,000 or more — numerous and excellent motels lining the Highway on the outskirts, two or three first-class hotels near the centre of things, and restaurants where the cuisine is adequate though rarely inspired. But to the stranger it is the reassurance that counts. The skyscrapers may not be as high as the ones back home but they are real, they exist. The public buildings are solid, occasionally impressive; they form walls against the menace of the all-but-empty space in which man's consequence is that of a handful of dust. The buildings can't shut out the sky, of course, but they impose limits on it.

If, however, you feel at home in the middle of vast empty spaces — and some people like myself do — you will resent Regina. And every other prairie city. They are alien eruptions on the face of nature, they disturb the harmony of a world in which the steel-and-glass ant-hills of modern man are an impertinence.

The massive domed Provincial Legislative Building — which looks exactly like dozens of other massive domed legislative buildings scattered over the continent — stands fronting an artificial lake. The lake is an always muddy and sometimes ill-smelling triumph of the human spirit; to create a body of water of any kind in Regina is an authentic miracle.

There are some things in Regina worth seeing. The splendid Museum of Natural History, one of the finest of its kind on the continent, is quite properly a source of civic and provincial pride; and the RCMP barracks, the western training centre for recruits to the Force, draws thousands of visitors during the summer months. An interesting museum is open to the public, and red-coated Mounties are always on exhibit during visiting hours.

For nine months of the year the citizens of Regina are a sober, well-ordered folk not much given to emotional display. The stranger will find little evidence among them of the backslapping exuberance alleged to be characteristic of the native Westerner. Their attitude towards sports is one of indifference; baseball they reject out of hand, hockey they barely tolerate. But in August a queer kind of madness falls upon the city; every other Saturday afternoon from early fall till late November — be it hot or cold or moist or dry — these same sober citizens and their fellows from as far away as Saskatoon and Prince Albert jam Taylor Field Stadium to urge on in a Bacchic frenzy the imported tanks on legs who are the

Saskatchewan Roughriders football team. Regina's passion for football is beyond the comprehension of the ordinary mortal. It needs a sociologist to explain it and a prairie Pindar to celebrate it.

Between Regina and Moose Jaw no islands of scrubby bush dot the surface of the immense sea of land — the great plains stretch uninterrupted to the perimeter of the horizon. This is the authentic wheat country, the original bread-basket of the world. The rich gumbo soil is an adhesive nightmare when wet but it produces the world's finest wheat — Number One Hard.

Moose Jaw squats in a tangle of ravines and valleys at the confluence of the Thunder and Moose Jaw creeks. The immensely wide main street is lined with substantial, reticent, old world buildings — the visitor from abroad subconsciously looks for a Lyons Corner House and a Barclay's Bank at every intersection. But the stolid, dignified appearance of the city is at odds with its reputation — in the roaring twenties Moose Jaw roared louder than any other town in the West. River Street was an internationally celebrated criminal hideout, half the city police force were arrested for various misdemeanours, and the Ku Klux Klan — whose Saskatchewan membership in the twenties is said to have numbered 40,000 — made Moose Jaw the centre of its prairie activities and proclaimed white supremacy and burned fiery crosses in a cow-pasture adjacent to the city.

Visitors interested in caged wildlife will no doubt enjoy the animal park which encloses 500 acres along the Moose Jaw Creek. But the enduring attraction of the city must always be its name. Moose Jaw, Saskatchewan, is an irresistible combination; like Medicine Hat and Walla Walla and Oshkosh, it lures from distant places seekers after the exotic, the off-beat. (My wife and I once made a detour of several hundred miles through rugged Wyoming mountain country for no other reason than to see what two towns named Spotted Horse and Ten Sleep looked like. Except for the bars, they looked exactly like any two Saskatchewan towns of comparable size.)

The name is said to be a creation of an Indian who observed a white man on the bank of the creek mending his broken cart with the jaw of a moose — a feat of improvisation well worth the Indian's attention. The story — to be regarded with the utmost respect and dubiety — was probably the creation of a publicity genius living in advance of his time.

West of Moose Jaw the Highway is bordered at frequent intervals by alkali sloughs. When the stagnant malodorous water evaporates it leaves a filmy white deposit which whips up in smoke-like clouds — sometimes deceiving the stranger into thinking he is running into a prairie fire — and dances in weird devil's jigs across the Highway. At Chaplin fifty miles west of Moose Jaw a sodium sulphate plant, one of several scattered throughout the province, squats in a dismal swamp of hell and converts the alkali deposits to commercial uses.

Swift Current, a hundred miles west of Moose Jaw, is a neon-bedecked oasis in a valley of dry bones, a pleasant stopping-place if the time is right. Swift Current is renowned in the West for its Dominion Experimental Station (the second-largest in Canada) and its boom-or-bust extravagances. Traditionally its citizens are either driving late-model Cadillacs or flat broke.

In 1885, the year of the Riel Rebellion, a force of Canadian militia detrained at Swift Current, then a huddle of shacks at the end of steel, and marched north to the relief of Battleford, for several weeks harassed by bands of Indians more intent on plunder than scalps. The militia under the command of Colonel Otter made the 150-mile march in five days, chased away the Indians, and were heroes for an hour. Unfortunately, and for no justifiable reason, Otter led his green youngsters into the Eagle Hills to punish Chief Poundmaker for failing to control his braves. The militia were badly defeated at Cutknife Hill and ironically escaped complete disaster only by courtesy of

Poundmaker who kept his exuberant warriors under the strictest control and refused to allow them to pursue the retreating enemy.

The Highway continues its course along a desolate valley-floor. The general pattern of landscape is unchanged; grain elevators still loom against the skyline and the next town is always in sight. But imperceptibly the valley widens, loses its outline; the road curves, rises, falls — and by-passes a town with the unlikely name of Piapot, so-called in honour of a Piegan chief who attempted to hold up the progress of the CPR (which he quite properly distrusted) by camping on the right-of-way. Inevitably he and his braves were removed without bloodshed by the ubiquitous Mounties — two of them.

To the traveller weary of elevators and grain-fields and the black ribbon snaking its way forever around low buttes and over sun-burnt ridges, the attraction of the land now lies to the south. Incredibly, a range of hills has come into view. They hang blue and remote between heaven and earth — but they are unmistakably real.

The Cypress Hills, occupying an area of over a thousand square miles, lie a few miles north of Montana and astride the Saskatchewan-Alberta border. They rise to a height of nearly 5,000 feet and form the highest point of land in Canada between Labrador and the Rockies. An island in the last ice-age — so some geologists theorize — the Hills constitute an unglaciated area which has preserved its own peculiar growths; there survive in the hills species of fauna and flora found nowhere else in Canada (many of them indigenous to regions hundreds of miles farther south). They include such exotic and alarming specimens of wildlife as solpugids (a species of scorpion), hog-nosed vipers, kangaroo rats, and black widow spiders. Fortunately these are all retiring creatures that live far off the beaten path in those parts of the hills and surrounding sun-baked terrain where yucca grass, prickly-pear cactus, and sagebrush flourish.

The Cypress Hills divide the American High Plains from that vast area of plain and forest and tundra once known as Prince Rupert's Land. There are points among the hills where it is possible for a man to stand and see streams flowing in opposite directions, to trace in the mind's eye the course of the south-bound water into the great Missouri-Mississippi system via the Milk River and on into the steaming Gulf of Mexico — or follow the north-bound streams across the great plains and into the Saskatchewan River basin to empty at last into the mist-haunted chill arctic indentation of Hudson Bay. Waters that have a common source end their journeyings five thousand miles apart — the Cypress Hills are quite literally the top of a continent.

In the days before the coming of the white man, the Cypress Hills country was a natural game sanctuary, and neutral ground between the Indian tribes who circled around the base of the hills and frequently penetrated them but never took permanent possession: the Cree and powerful Blackfoot Confederacy to the north and west, the Assiniboine, Crow, Nez Percé, and Sioux to the east and south. Palliser was the first white man to report on the hills — "a perfect oasis in the desert we have travelled." Métis moving out of Red River following the disturbances of 1870-1 found a pastoral paradise among the hills, although the majority of those who made the trek west preferred to settle several hundred miles farther north. The Hudson's Bay Company established a post in the hills in 1871 but abandoned it the following year, leaving the fur trade to the independents from across the border who, unlike the Great Company, were happy to swap whisky for furs. The massacre of a large band of Assiniboine Indians by drunken traders in 1873 hastened the formation of the North West Mounted Police; and three years later the red-coats built Fort Walsh in the heart of the hills. The law had come to stay.

No tourist, however rushed, should miss spending at least a

day among the hills, for they encompass within their modest limits more history, more authentic folklore, and more unique charm than any comparable area in the West. Maple Creek, a sleepy, rather un-Western looking town — the public buildings are brick, the houses old, the streets pleasantly shaded — is the turning-off place for the hills. The highway south (No. 21) rises steadily over a stretch of twenty miles to a height of 4,000 feet and a point where a rustic gate invites entry into the Cypress Hills Provincial Park.

My family and I first visited the park many years ago, and the memory of that experience still lingers like a gracious benediction — a memory of the rich, rank smells of evergreen and woodsmoke and bacon frying over a pot-bellied stove in an unvarnished old log hut; of the sight of water fringed on all sides by tall lodge-pine (a miracle in south-western Saskatchewan); and of a sunset view over half Saskatchewan from an eminence prosaically called Bald Butte, a view so softened, magical in the half light — all harsh geometric lines subdued, blatant colours modified — as to suggest that Bald Butte must have been the point from which the devil tempted Christ with a view of all the kingdoms of the earth. The memory of that first evening has drawn us back to the hills summer after summer; they are to us the best-known, best-loved region of the West.

The park facilities are unimpressive and the tiny lake around which they cluster isn't much good for swimming or fishing. But the hills themselves are what matter. Perhaps the most exciting short drive in Saskatchewan is the one leading south-west from the park over a winding dirt road for twenty odd miles to Fort Walsh. Herds of white-faces dot the slopes as far as the eye can see, grazing knee-deep in the lush grass of the wide valley bottoms (the hills average four inches more of moisture per year than the surrounding plains), and as likely as not a herd of antelope will come into view on a far-off ridge. The road snakes its way across hills and ravines and through a ranchman's yard, winds up a precipitous slope to a high plateau, then plunges down the other side into the valley of the Battle Creek.

Fort Walsh, named in honour of one of the first commissioners of the North West Mounted Police, was built in the valley of the Battle in 1876. None too soon, for 1876 was a bad year in the hills. The great buffalo herds had all but vanished from the surrounding plains, and hunger drove the Indians into the hills where a few herds still survived. Here the Indian made his last stand in the West for the way of life he knew and loved; here on the neutral ground lived uneasily the tribes from the adjacent Canadian plains, side by side with hordes of sullen, restless refugees from across the American border. Here in 1876 came Sitting Bull and his fierce Sioux warriors, fresh from their triumph over the cream of the U.S. cavalry at the Battle of the Little Big Horn; and here a handful of men in red coats fed the hungry, proclaimed the Queen's law, and compelled white man and Indian alike to accept it.

Old Fort Walsh has long since disappeared. The fort standing in the valley today is not a restoration but a reconstruction. The barracks, stables, guard-room, kitchens, palisades are built to scale and no doubt provide an accurate visual picture of the original. But the spirit of the past lingers uneasily if at all among these shiny, painted replicas; its true dwelling-place is the abiding hills, and the little graveyard a few hundred yards from Fort Walsh, on the rim of the great valley.

In the graveyard lie the bodies of a dozen or more of the men of the North West Mounted Police. What is significant about the inscriptions engraved on the modest headstones is this: only one records death by violence. Constable Marmaduke Graeburn, aged nineteen, was murdered; the others in the graveyard died prosaically of pneumonia and dysentery and typhoid. Indirectly these inscriptions constitute the highest tribute that can be paid to the men who in 1876 went into the hills, for they make it clear that they went not to fight the Indians but to save them.

The peaceful settlement of the Canadian West by contrast with the violence which marked the opening of the American frontier stemmed in part from the foresight of the Dominion government in placing a force of policemen on the prairies well in advance of the main tide of settlers. On the American frontier army forces arrived long after savage warfare between white man and Indian had become part of the frontier pattern; and many of the army men, veterans of four years' atrocious civil conflict, assumed that the simplest way to establish peace was to kill all the Indians. But much of the credit for the peaceful settlement of the Canadian West must go to the men of the original police force. Their courage and endurance were beyond question; and most of the members, particularly those with Old Country backgrounds, assumed almost by instinct the role of guardians. . . . Lieutenant William Butler, the British Army officer who accompanied Colonel Wolseley to Winnipeg and afterwards investigated conditions prevailing among the Plains Indians and traders, reported in 1871 that a force of not more than 150 men was needed to maintain order throughout the territory reaching from the eastern Manitoba border to the Rockies. Butler had seen service in many outposts of empire including India, and his faith in the power and integrity of men doing the work of empire touches either the ridiculous or the sublime — perhaps a little of both. That faith was shared by the members of the Force and countless times it carried them triumphantly and without bloodshed through situations which seemed certain to end in fighting and death. Thcy were the kind of men from whose exploits great legends spring. In a time when it has become fashionable to denigrate the achievements of the old North West Mounted Police we would do well to remember that legends contain the essence of truth.

In the long run, the Mounties failed to save the Indian, but only because not even men in red coats could reverse the immutable course of history.

The obvious way to leave Saskatchewan and enter Alberta is by the Highway through the border town of Walsh a few miles west of Maple Creek. But those travellers who long for a few hours' escape from gas fumes and asphalt and high speeds should do as my wife and I did on our trans-Canada journey — make the crossing by way of the winding municipal roads and rutted private trails that haphazardly link the Cypress Hills Provincial Park on the Saskatchewan side with Elkwater Park in Alberta, twenty-five miles south of the Highway and forty-odd miles from Medicine Hat. It is a route — unofficial, mostly unmarked — that takes you past Fort Walsh and out of the valley of the Battle up on to high, bare ridges from which immense vistas open up both north and south, bringing into view on a clear day the Bearpaw Mountains in Montana. It gives you a chance, too, to meet authentic ranchers and cow-pokes, for you are sure to get lost several times and will have to ask your way. ("Just take that trail over the hill," one weather-beaten cow-hand told us. "She'll drop you down the other side into so-and-so's back yard." She did, too. Literally — our faithful car leaning back like a well-trained mustang and digging in her heels all the way down.)

Some day, no doubt, an excellent paved road impossible to stray from will link the two parks; but for a few years longer the crazy trails snaking among the rounded hills and over the great ridges will enable us to slip back into a world which — except for the occasional jet streaking across the heavens — differs hardly at all from the one Lieutenant William Butler saw nearly a century ago and described better than anyone before or since, in his classic of western travel, *The Great Lone Land:*

"The great ocean itself does not present more infinite variety than does this prairie-ocean of which we speak. In winter, a dazzling surface of purest snow; in early summer, a vast expanse of grass and pale pink roses; in autumn too often a wild sea of raging fire. No ocean of water in the world can vie with its gorgeous sunsets; no solitude can equal the loneliness of a night-shadowed prairie; one feels the stillness and hears the silence, the wail of the prowling wolf makes the voice of solitude audible, the stars look down through infinite silence on a silence almost as intense . . . But for my part, the prairies had nothing terrible in their aspect, nothing oppressive in their loneliness. One saw here the world as it had taken shape and form from the hands of the Creator. Nor did the scene look less beautiful because nature alone tilled the earth, and the unaided sun brought forth the flowers."

The Hotel in Ituna

Glen Sorestad

Outside the wheatfields roll like a Commons speech
rocking green-gold in the shortening of summer
and the wind sucks the tongue as dry as noon.

Inside the hotel a mural stretches the long wall
into a Hawaiian beach, hand-painted by an Indian
who saw the picture once on an American postcard.

Alberta

Edward A. McCourt

Medicine Hat is a name and a story. It is a few other things besides. It is the first important town on the Trans-Canada Highway inside the Alberta border; and — although unfortunately identified in the public mind with a plethora of publicity-conscious rain-makers, flagpole sitters, and extrovert mayors — a pleasant place to live in and pleasing to the eye.

Sprawled along the flats and banks of the South Saskatchewan River in the middle of a vast semi-arid region given over mainly to ranching, Medicine Hat is a cow-town in spirit and in fact, and an industrial centre of some importance because of its unlimited supply of natural gas. But the name and the story are what matter.

A dozen legends, none altogether convincing, explain the name. The saving of the name is the story.

In 1907 Rudyard Kipling, then at the height of his fame (he had just won the Nobel Prize), stopped off in Medicine Hat while on a trans-Canada tour. The members of the Cypress Club, mostly old-timers of assorted occupations and political views, took Kipling in hand and saved him from the horrors of an orthodox civic reception. "We just met him as man to man, in all our rustic habits," a member of the club reported. "We talked to him as if he was a beef buyer and really had a whale of a time. Of course R. K. ate it up and hated to tear himself away." The great man showed his immediate appreciation of the club's hospitality by coining a catch-phrase used ever since to describe Medicine Hat — "the city with all hell for a basement". But the really grand gesture was yet to come.

Three years after Kipling's visit, Medicine Hat experienced the building-and-real-estate boom inevitable in a Western town near the beginning of the century. The boom lasted just long enough to flood the town with dull-spirited, ignorant new-comers who denounced its name as an embarrassing absurdity and demanded that it be changed forthwith to something respectable, something "that has a sound like the name of a man's best girl and looks like business at the head of the financial report" — to quote *The Calgary Herald,* which had no business butting in. The city council, conventional hustling business types to a man, ordered a plebiscite to settle the issue. Those stout upholders of the ancient ways, the members of the Cypress Club, knowing the outcome of the plebiscite to be a foregone conclusion and the triumph of respectability over tradition inevitable, were morose and disconsolate men until at a wake in the club-rooms a member, whose name unfortunately has been lost in the mists of time, raised from his beer-mug a face suddenly illumined with a deep and holy joy and said, "Kipling should know of this — he'd flay the hide off those blighters."

The thought was instantly translated into action. The club member delegated to write to Kipling was the local postmaster, Frank Fatt. An excellent choice, for Mr. Fatt was no mean hand with a pen. His letter is an eloquent plea to "the Father Confessor of the Empire" to save the name of the town on behalf of the old-timers. "Here we have courted our sweethearts, married and begot children and built our homes, driving our tent pegs deep into Mother Earth," Mr. Fatt cried out in impassioned accents, "and here we remain to hold up the old British tradition as long as the good God gives us breath."

Mr. Fatt's plea is not, however, entirely sentimental rhapsody — he reveals a pretty talent himself for flaying the hides off the new-comers, "the sons of Belial who have arisen and want to change the name of the city. It smacks too much of the Injun, smells fearfully of the tepee fire and kini-ki-nick, reminds outsiders of the whacking lies (may God forgive them) of the US newspaper men in regard to our weather and so forth. In a moment of weakness our city fathers have decided to submit the question to the vote of the ratepayers instead of ordering the proposers to be cast into a den of fiery rattlesnakes."

Then follows the appeal direct:

"Can you help us with a few words of encouragement in combating these heretics? Your influence here is great. If it is shown that you are against this proposition, it will help us materially."

Kipling obliged. His letter to Mr. Fatt, dated from

Bateman's Burwash, Sussex, is a devastating combination of sentiment, logic, and invective. It deserves to be quoted at length:

"... You tell me that a public vote is to be taken on the question of changing the city's name. So far as I can make out ... the chief arguments for the change are (a) that some US journalists have some sort of joke that Medicine Hat supplies all the bad weather of the US and (b) that another name would look better at the head of a prospectus. ...

"Now as to the charge of brewing bad weather, etc., I see no reason on earth why white men should be fluffed out of their city's birthright by an imported joke. Accept the charge joyously and proudly and go forward as Medicine Hat — the only city officially recognized as capable of freezing out the United States and giving the continent cold feet. ...

"To my mind the name of Medicine Hat ... echoes as you so justly put it the old Cree and Blackfoot tradition of red mystery and romance that once filled the prairies. ... Believe me, the very name is an asset, and as years go on will become more and more of an asset. It has no duplicate in the world; it makes men ask questions ... draws the feet of young men towards it; it has the qualities of uniqueness, individuality, assertion, and power. Above all, it is the lawful, original, sweat-and-dust-won name of the city, and to change it would be to risk the luck of the city, to disgust and dishearten old-timers, not in the city alone, but the world over, and to advertise abroad the city's lack of faith in itself. Men do not think much of a family which has risen in the world, changing its name for social reasons. They think still less of a man who because he is successful repudiates the wife who stood by him in his early struggles. I do not know what I should say, but I have the clearest notion of what I should think of a town that went back on itself. ...

"In conclusion, it strikes me that the two arguments put forward for the change of the name are almost equally bad. The second is perhaps a shade worse than the first. In the first case the town would change its name in the hope of making more money under an alias or, as *The Calgary Herald* writes, for the sake of a name that 'has a sound like the name of a man's best girl and looks like business at the head of a financial report.'

"But a man's city is a trifle more than a man's best girl. She is the living background of his life and love and toil and hope and sorrow and joy. Her success is his success; her shame is his shame; her honour is his honour; and her good name is his good name.

"What, then, should a city be rechristened that has sold its name? Judasville."

The members of the Cypress Club saw to it that Kipling's letter was given nation-wide publicity and the sons of Belial were silenced. They have remained silent ever since.

Recently Mr. E. J. Goodwin, editor of the Medicine Hat *News,* performed a fine public service when he compiled a pamphlet, free to anyone dropping into the *News* office, containing the complete Fatt-Kipling correspondence.

Medicine Hat is near the centre of the Canadian shortgrass country — the third Prairie Steppe — a lonely, desolate plain furrowed by dry, eroded coulees where nothing grows except tufted short-grass and sagebrush and greasewood and prickly-pear cactus. Attempts to dry-farm the short-grass country have drawn bitter comments from the cattlemen who just naturally hate farmers anyway — "Ain't it a shame how them damn weasels have tore up all the country north of the Bow? She's so bloody gravelly underneath she won't grow grass for a goose, and them simple farmers expect to grow wheat!" So far the attempts appear largely unsuccessful. There are stretches of the Highway between Medicine Hat and Brooks, seventy miles farther north-west, where literally nothing breaks the monotony of the prairie land except the Highway and the telephone line. Not a tree, house, or living creature disturbs the surface of a plain rolling to the most distant horizon the eye ever strained to reach. It is while driving over such stretches that individuals of a gregarious nature develop an intense affection for a strip of asphalt. The Highway becomes a symbol of humanity in a land virtually devoid of all other suggestion of life.

There are places on the earth that assume immense importance not because of *what* they are but *where*. Brooks, Alberta, is one of these places. It is the centre of an irrigation district, the site of a horticultural experimental station, a town of tree-lined streets and lush green lawns in the middle of a treeless, barren desolation. But anyone wishing to see the epitome of man's determination to make the desert rejoice and blossom like the rose should leave the town and drive south ten miles to Lake Newall and Kinbrook Park.

Kinbrook Park is an artificial island rising from an artificial lake and studded with thousands of hand-planted trees. Lake Newall is a great reservoir covering forty square miles, created by pouring water from the dammed-up Bow River into a depression on the prairie; the island is a ridge of land surmounting the surrounding depression.

Judged by the standards prevailing in moister parts of the earth, Kinbrook Park is no beauty spot. The trees are mostly small and scraggly, the surrounding landscape featureless, the cottages huddled along the lakeshore a gaudy-hued offence to aesthetic sensibilities (several of them are painted a curious piebald, no doubt a reflection of cow-country influence). No beauty spot, but a genuine phenomenon. The lake is clear and deep, the artificially created sand beaches of generous expanse, the picnic- and camp-site facilities excellent. Fishing is an advertised attraction, but after a conversation in the park with a man from North Dakota I hesitate to recommend it.

The man from North Dakota was drunk. At five in the afternoon. "Got the flu," he explained. "Gives a man the shakes.'' He stared at the lake with bloodshot eyes. ''Come up for the fishin','' he said after a while. ''Fishin's no damn good.'' ''Wrong time of year,'' I suggested wisely, but the man from North Dakota paid me no heed. ''Been comin' here every year for thirteen year,'' he said. ''Fishin's never any damn good.''

I pondered. Why should a man come all the way from North Dakota for thirteen years straight to fish an artificial lake in the middle of an Alberta desert? No doubt any body of water would be a marvel to a man from North Dakota, but there were several a good deal nearer home. But I did not ask any questions for I had no wish to pry into the secret places of his soul. Every man, I suppose, pursues in his own peculiar fashion his own peculiar Grail.

Kinbrook Park is a man-made wonder. Thirty miles north-east of Brooks lies a natural wonder which the traveller who relishes the unexpected and spectacular should spend an hour or two exploring.

The gravelled municipal road to the Steveville Dinosaur Park cuts through irrigated farmlands past farmsteads all of which look alike. Gorgeously coloured pheasants stroll across the road introducing a touch of the exotic, the bizarre, into an otherwise prosaic, neatly patterned world of squares, rectangles, and identical windbreaks. Brooks is the centre of a famous pheasant hatchery, and every fall, hunters, many of them from the United States, swarm into the district for the annual pheasant slaughter which no doubt is excellent for business.

Like so many natural phenomena of the prairies, the badlands of the Red Deer River burst upon you without the slightest warning. Steveville Dinosaur Park is a Dantesque nightmare, a wild eerie region of eroded hoodoos, fantastically distorted monstrous shapes of earth rising from the valley-floor between towering canyon walls. Along the valley-floor the Red Deer River runs sluggishly past dismal sagebrush flats, and the stunted trees lining its banks have been twisted by wind and flood into grotesque witch-figures fit to haunt a man's sleep if seen by moonlight.

The badlands of the Red Deer are an authentic valley of dry bones. Most of the region has been well picked over in the past thirty or forty years, but anyone with enough enthusiasm and energy to dig in an out-of-the-way spot may be lucky enough to make a bone-strike. Several skeletons of prehistoric monsters are on exhibit within the park, including the fenced-in remains of a "Duckbill Dinosaur, *laying* just as found" (italics mine).

No doubt for most visitors the attraction of the Steveville Dinosaur Park palls after an hour or two because the region is so completely devoid of human associations. The Indians avoided it like the plague, and the Canadian West never nurtured the kind of bad man who might have been driven to seek refuge there. Similar regions in Montana and Wyoming have resounded to the thunder of hooves and the crack of Winchesters and the whirring of movie-cameras, but the only sound to disturb the silence of the Red Deer badlands for ages past has been the clank of the excavator's shovel. The entire valley from Steveville to Drumheller, a hundred miles north-west, is one vast prehistoric graveyard.

A few miles west of Brooks the contour of the land changes — or perhaps it would be more accurate to say it acquires contours. The Bow River valley dominates the landscape, rising in precipitous bluffs and vast rolling swells to relieve the monotony of the great plain. Four miles off the Highway and three miles south of the village of Cluny is a spot splendid to look at, rich in history — the very heart of the Blackfoot country. Only a man insensitive to beauty and with no concern for the romance and heartbreak of time past can look down the long valley-slope to the old Blackfoot Crossing and remain unmoved.

Here from time immemorial the Indians of the Blackfoot

Confederacy crossed the Bow River on their endless north-south journeyings; here they rendezvoused, pitched their tents, plotted war against their ancient enemies the Crees, and sometimes smoked the pipe of peace. And here in the year 1877 on the south bank of the river they signed away their heritage, the land of their ancestors.

On a high bluff overlooking the Crossing a cairn commemorates the signing of Blackfoot Treaty Number Seven. On that day in 1877, 4,000 Indians of the Blackfoot Confederacy — Blackfoot, Blood, Stony, Piegan, Sarcee — pitched their tents at the Crossing, and there the great Chief Crowfoot and his fellows met in solemn council with the commissioners of the Great White Queen. Nearly a hundred members of the North West Mounted Police added to the pomp and pageantry of a ceremony which marked the end of a long day's dying — the day of the Indian. Crowfoot and his people, in return for a few scattered reserves and five dollars a year of treaty money, surrendered to the Queen, "for as long as the sun shines and rivers run", the land which is now south-western Alberta.

Romantic souls who share Cyrano de Bergerac's view that "one does not fight because there is hope of winning — it is much finer to fight when it is no use" may feel that Crowfoot would have done better to lead his people, like Sitting Bull and Chief Joseph of the Nez Percé, in one last desperate campaign against the white intruder, rather than submit tamely to his demands. Had he done so the history of the Canadian West would have been more colourful because bloodier. But Crowfoot was not a romantic, he was a realist who accepted the inevitable. By 1877 the buffalo had all but disappeared from the prairie and with their going the old way of life went too. Crowfoot was no lover of the white man but he saw in him the only hope of salvation for his people. And having pledged his word he kept it. When, eight years after the signing of the treaty, the Métis under Louis Riel set the West aflame,

Crowfoot refused to give ear to Riel's emissaries and held his restless, disillusioned braves in check. The Council of the Northwest Territories rewarded Crowfoot for his loyalty with a gift of fifty dollars and the CPR gave him a lifetime pass that he hardly ever used.

Perhaps had Crowfoot foreseen the fate of his people he would have gone down fighting.

Crowfoot lived out his last years on the Blackfoot reservation near the Crossing. A memorial plaque on the valley's rim marks the spot to which the great chief, feeling death upon him, was carried to look for the last time on the valley and the Crossing. (Just as another aristocrat, Sir Walter Scott — who would have admired Crowfoot — paused on his last sad journey to Abbotsford to bid farewell to his beloved Tweed.) Crowfoot must have yielded reluctantly to death, knowing that he would find no fairer land in any Happy Hunting Ground. The valley swells in great folds to meet the immensity of over-arching sky, and the river snakes along the valley-floor, flowing from the far-off mountains that serrate the western skyline — white wave-crests frozen into eternal stillness. A great land to live in. A land hard to leave.

Crowfoot is buried in the Indian graveyard that overlooks the Crossing from a high bluff. The graveyard is an austere and melancholy spot. Most of the graves are unmarked, but one massive slab to the memory of James Drunken Cheif (*sic*) stirs at least casual curiosity. A stone cairn inscribed with the meaningless phrase "Father of his People" commemorates Crowfoot.

There are one or two other Crowfoot memorials in the vicinity of the Crossing, including a dingy railway whistle-stop (two grain elevators and a station-house) and a muddy creek. Thirty miles east, the attractive irrigation town of Bassano commemorates the name of an Italian nobleman, and it is just possible that the contrast between the Crowfoot and Bassano memorials may give rise to some interesting reflections on our sense of values. Crowfoot was merely the last great chief of a once-great people, but the Marquis de Bassano held shares in the CPR.

The Highway side-swipes Calgary along her northern flank and it is easy to by-pass the city. Few of us are likely to do so, for Calgary is one of the two glamour cities of Canada. (The other is, of course, Montreal.) Her history is prosaic — a record of steady, sometimes spectacular growth from Mounted Police fort (1875) to cow-town to oil-town. But the great Calgary Stampede, Canada's most celebrated annual show, has given the city nearly world-wide publicity. The white Stetson hat has become her symbol, cow-town her *nom de plume*. Even the athletic teams that represent the city are invariably Broncos or Stampeders and they play hockey in the Corral. To the hundreds of thousands of visitors who throng the Stampede grounds and the thousands of passing tourists who don't stay long enough to learn the truth, Calgary epitomizes the spirit and tradition of the old West.

Calgary enjoys what is perhaps the finest scenic location of all our cities — only Quebec, Montreal, and Vancouver can offer serious competition. The Bow and Elbow rivers form a junction near her heart, the foothills roll away in great hump-backed swells on three sides, and on the fourth the wide valley of the Bow reaches back to the mountains sixty miles west, and the mountains, abrupt, massive, snow-capped, form a stunning backdrop against the wide sky.

The city itself is unworthy of its setting. Architecturally Calgary is a stereotype of the typical modern big town. Office skyscrapers no more or less imaginative than the general run dominate the city's centre, and the fungus-like growths of suburbia blotch the fair face of the Bow River valley and surrounding hill-sides. Unlike such western United States cities as Denver and Salt Lake City, Calgary takes no colour from her surroundings — she is Regina or Moose Jaw or Lethbridge cast in a larger mould. She sits at the very heart of a great range country, but a cowboy is seldom seen on her main streets, and when he does appear he is an anachronism. His true Saturday-night home of the spirit is the small, authentic cow-town like Medicine Hat or Maple Creek.

The truth is that Calgary is not a cow-town any more but a booming oil-town and one of Canada's important financial centres. Making money is Calgary's real business. The Turner Valley oil strike of 1913 laid the foundation of the modern city's prosperity and determined her view and way of life. Oil in the immediate vicinity has long since petered out but most of the great oil companies and scores of smaller ones maintain their western headquarters in Calgary. The man in the white Stetson hat, cowboy boots, and Cadillac is nine times out of ten an oil tycoon.

Apart from making money, the favourite pastime of Calgarians is feuding with Edmonton, the capital city of the province. Calgary has never forgiven Edmonton for being both provincial capital and the site of the provincial university. (Things were much better arranged in Saskatchewan — Regina got the Legislature, Saskatoon the University; as a result inter-city squabbling has been generally spasmodic and amicable.) But the feuding between the Alberta cities is sustained and seldom good-humoured. On the Calgary side, at least, it is now carried on in a spirit which reflects an odd combination of mature satiric wit and adolescent pique — a spirit admirably illustrated by an editorial in a Calgary paper attacking Edmonton's admittedly absurd effort to jazz up its 1963 Exhibition by introducing a Klondike Days motif:

". . . This is casting about for identity with a vengeance. In the field of capitalizing on someone else's glamorous past, this probably will forever stand as a world record.

"By what kind of yardstick, by what devious reasoning, can Edmonton be linked with the Klondike and its gold? . . .

"We're tempted to ask, when you think of Edmonton, what

do you think of? Instead, we will state flatly that when you think of Edmonton, gold you most certainly do not think of.

"Snowdrifts, maybe, or iceworms. But not gold, by any stretch of the imagination. . . .

"It was possible to sympathize with Edmonton's search for a soul. But in attempting to emulate Calgary (which wisely chose to glorify its authentic heritage), Edmonton has emerged as a city of desperation.

"Even Calgary could stage a Klondike Days with a truer ring. At least the citizens here enjoy a certain affluence.

"Why doesn't Edmonton just put up a booth at the Calgary Stampede and forget about trying to do something on its own?"

Calgary's decision to "glorify its authentic heritage" has been a money-making proposition. But let no innocent visitor to the Stampede be deceived into thinking that he is watching the true sons of the Canadian West in action. The star performers before the grandstand — except the chuckwagon drivers — are nearly all hardbitten professional entertainers who follow the great summer rodeo circuit over half the continent, ending up in Madison Square Garden. Local small-town rodeos, and there are many of them, lack the glamour and the hysterical excitement of the Second Greatest Show on Earth, but they are in many ways more rewarding for they reflect to a far greater degree the authentic spirit of the range country.

Calgary is a bright, airy, obvious town, all her wares on display, no unexpected delights hidden around corners. Although she boasts a university, a symphony orchestra, a fine arts centre, and numerous other adjuncts of conventional culture, it is safe to say that Calgary has no wish to be the Athens of the West. She would much sooner be the Houston.

But let not her frailties be remembered. Calgary women are among the most beautiful in Canada and, outside Montreal, the best dressed.

Calgary caters admirably to tourists. Other cities are content to settle for a motel strip — Calgary, characteristically, boasts a motel village. It is conveniently located at the junction of the Trans-Canada Highway and No. 1A; and there, except during Stampede Week, the tourist is almost certain to find adequate accommodation.

Driving the Highway from Calgary into the mountains can be a dangerous experience. The Highway itself is new, superbly engineered, adequately posted — the hazards are scenic rather than technical. The temptations to take your eye from the road ahead are frequent and almost irresistible, but resisted they must be, for the flow of traffic is sure to be heavy. Tourists swarm across the border into southern Alberta and up the Fort Macleod-Calgary Trail to join the hordes from the East already pounding towards the mountains at seventy miles an hour. Unfortunately — and this is the only possible criticism of the Trans-Canada Highway between Calgary and Banff — look-outs are few, and the man behind the wheel must be content to observe in disconnected snatches the stupendous wall of mountain ahead.

On the Calgary-Banff run the Highway passes through splendidly uncluttered country, much of it an Indian reserve. Thirty miles out of Calgary, a side-road leads across the Bow River to the Stony Indian settlement of Morley, and the little church built by the missionaries George MacDougall and his son John in 1872. The church, unused since 1921, has recently been restored and stands out bravely in its new coat of white and green paint on the bare north bank of the rushing Bow. The tourist pavilion that has been built immediately adjacent to the church may appear an incongruity unless we can bring ourselves to regard it as an up-to-date parish hall.

Four years after building the church the Rev. George MacDougall died in a blizzard at a spot a few miles north of the church-site.

MacDougall's church stands beside the old Banff highway, now numbered 1A, and familiarly called the Banff Trail. In some respects the old highway is even more scenic than the new — at certain points it affords a broader panorama embracing the entire sweep of the Bow Valley and the mountains beyond. One of the finest views in all Canada is that from the turn-out at the top of the great hill above the village of Cochrane twenty miles west of Calgary — a magnificent expanse of river, valley, foothills, mountains, and over-arching sky juxtaposed in a flawlessly balanced harmony, so flawless as to suggest a deliberately contrived artistic improvement on nature. It is a view of which no man can ever tire, for although the elements are fixed, permanent, the colour- and cloud-patterns change minute by minute so that the communicated effect is of something at once enduring and at the same time forever new.

The forestry road into the Kananaskis Forest Reserve lying south of the Highway provides another admirable diversion for the adventurous traveller. The turn-off, marked by a garage, a store, and a modest sign, is easy to miss. The gravelled road runs a total of 139 miles south to the town of Coleman in the Crowsnest Pass, but for the Trans-Canada traveller a side-trip to the nearest camp-site — about twenty miles — will be enough to assure him that the relatively unpublicized Kananaskis Forest Reserve is one of the most magnificent and least cluttered mountain and lake regions in all Canada. The mountains west of the road rise to a height of over 11,000 feet — higher than at Banff. The road is sometimes rough in spots but always safe; and driving over it for even a few miles satisfies the urge in all of us to do something a little different, off-beat — permits us to cherish a secret delight knowing that nearly everyone else is tearing straight on for Banff.

The plainsman like myself is likely to find his first plunge into the mountains on the Calgary-Banff run an alarming experience. Not because of the Highway gradients, which are gentle, nor the curves, which are also gentle and well-banked, but because of the sudden feeling of being separated from all familiar things. Before we are aware of what is happening the beautiful but sinister Three Sisters and assorted kinfolk have slipped in behind us and cut off our retreat. But the valley ahead broadens — there is still room to breathe. We are not yet fenced in. Not quite.

Canmore is the only town between Calgary and Banff. Once a flourishing mining community, it now survives by means invisible to mortal sight. The ardent student of Canadiana should, however, slip off the Highway long enough to look at Canmore's modest United Church. A missionary named Charles Gordon was its builder and first minister; tradition alleges that young Gordon, better known to the world as Ralph Connor, wrote his first novel, *Black Rock: A Tale of the Selkirks,* in the study of the little church. The tradition is inaccurate — *Black Rock* was written in Winnipeg — but the basic material of the novel and several others including *The Sky Pilot* and *The Prospector* stems from the young missionary's experiences during the four years he was in charge of the Banff pastorate, a district covering 20,000 square miles of mountain and foothill.

No doubt the present generation knows not Joseph, but Ralph Connor deserves to be remembered in a money-conscious age if only because he was the first and almost only Canadian to make a small fortune from his books. *Black Rock* alone, originally intended as a series of sketches describing life in a western mining town and reshaped into the semblance of a novel, sold over 300,000 copies.

The Canmore United — originally Presbyterian — Church, built under the direction of Ralph Connor, is one more reminder — there are many throughout the West — of the influence of the missionaries on the development of Western Canada from the early days of the nineteenth century. Thomas Rundle carried the Word to the Blackfoot of the Banff district as early as 1840 — his memorial is the grand mountain towering over the valley of the Bow a few miles east of Banff. The MacDougalls, Father Lacombe, and a dozen other stout-hearted champions of the Cross roamed the plains and mountain valleys, founded their missions, fought the whisky-traders, and saved from destruction many Indian bodies and perhaps a few souls. In the restored frontier towns of the western United States the saloons, honky-tonks, and Boot Hills predominate, in western Canada the mission churches and Mounted Police posts. Strong men of God worked hand in hand with the Mounties to make the Canadian West a tough place for sinners.

It still is.

Most of us travelling the Trans-Canada Highway on holiday have certain objectives firmly rooted in the conscious or subconscious mind. Of these objectives Banff is certainly the most obvious and popular. It is the oldest, the best-known, and the best-loved national park in Canada.

Even the most jaded sophisticate must acknowledge that Banff is one of the loveliest spots on earth. Indeed, looking at the town and its environs from the summit of Sulphur Mountain you get the curious impression that in creating Banff, God assumed the role of a far-sighted parks superintendent and designed the area with a view to future tourism: planting a small, easily accessible mountain or two near the heart of things, a couple of larger ones — Rundle and Cascade — for scenic purposes at opposite ends of the town, directing a river, complete with picturesque falls yet suitable for boating, down a broad valley, studding the valley-floor and lower mountain-sides with magnificent evergreen forests (but leaving enough open space for a golf course), carving out a spectacular canyon or two within easy walking distance of the future town-site, banking the valley at both ends with solid mountain masses, and — the final touch of God-like benevolence — laying on an abundant supply of water, hot and cold.

Man has carried on the Creator's work with admirable discretion and good taste. The town of Banff appears characterless by design; and there is wisdom in such planning, for in such a setting the man-made could impose itself only through incongruity. The town buildings, both public and private, are unostentatious and so are the tourist accommodations. The many motels and hotels and private boarding-houses are comfortable — in a few instances luxurious — but all melt modestly into their environment, become a part of it. Even the neon lights seem subdued, their colours mostly soft pastels. The garish, the ornate, the ugly find no place in Banff.

With one exception. The Banff Springs Hotel sits overlooking the Bow Valley like a dowager duchess, an ageless relic of a bygone age casting an undimmed eye over the possessions she shares with no one — not even God. The hotel was almost completely rebuilt in 1928, but the remodellers worked in the spirit of an earlier and more grandiose time. Sir William Van Horne, who insisted that the original hotel be built in imitation of a French chateau to honour the early French fur-traders (few of whom had ever seen a chateau), would have approved the present design.

For those who can afford it — mostly Americans — the hotel provides all the amenities. But her chief value — impossible to think of a duchess as neuter — is as an act of defiance, a symbol of man's determination to impose something of himself, preserve his identity among the most awe-inspiring works of nature. Somerset Maugham has remarked that perfection is always a little dull; and perhaps the charm of the Banff Springs Hotel lies in her very incongruity — she adds the one essential touch of the freakish which prevents the perfection of Banff from becoming tiresome. For, whatever emotions she may arouse in those who contemplate her, boredom is certainly not one of them.

It is a tribute to those in charge of the park that even in the height of the tourist season Banff is a tranquil place. Night-life is almost non-existent — high altitudes and long walks (which can hardly be resisted) conspire to early and child-like slumber. The smell of evergreen overpowers the gas fumes, and you go to bed nearly everywhere within sound of running water — nature's ultimate soporific.

Even the wild animals behave with dignity and decorum in Banff National Park. Banff bears in no way resemble their alleged kinfolk in, say, Yellowstone. Yellowstone bears are overstuffed, revolting, moth-eaten panhandlers who snarl up traffic for miles while pursuing their gluttonous inclinations and make the night hideous by overturning garbage cans in search of snacks to ward off night starvation. Banff bears raid garbage cans too, but they lift the lids off very quietly. And they never hold up traffic. They prefer to walk at twilight along a forest path a few paces behind an unsuspecting tourist who is likely to lose a week's growth if he happens to turn around.

Banff bears have a sense of humour.

The chair-lift to the top of Mount Norquay carries one into regions of air otherwise inaccessible except to dyed-in-the-wool mountain-climbers; but the gondola to the top of Sulphur Mountain, a modest 8,000-foot hump overlooking the town-site, is a concession to modern softness. Such a contraption is morally permissible only to old-age pensioners and arthritics, but most of the customers appear under twenty-one and in sound health.

Lake Louise, forty miles west of Banff, is a place familiar to all Canadians and most Americans even though they have never visited it, for it is surely the most photographed beauty-spot on the continent and it looks exactly like its photographs. Word-pictures of the lake are almost as numerous and banal as the photographs, but one of the earliest, written by Rupert Brooke in 1913, has had some odd repercussions in our own time. A literature text-book adopted for use in Alberta schools a year or so ago included the Rupert Brooke description, but with one significant omission. Brooke's words — "Banff is an ordinary little tourist resort in mountainous country, with hills and a stream and snow peaks beyond. Beautiful enough and invigorating. But Lake Louise — Lake Louise is of another world'' — were made to read, ''Banff . . . is beautiful enough and invigorating.'' The general editor of the text-book defended himself and his committee against the attacks of the purists on the grounds that Brooke's essay was badly dated and that the parts deleted ''didn't add [to] but detracted'' from its value. He also pointed out that it is customary for editorial committees to delete ''offensive'' passages from the plays of William Shakespeare.

The mountains surrounding Lake Louise are splendid to look at and uncomfortable to live with. Mountains, I feel, are unsuitable companions for the daily round. For they have nothing in common with temporal things — they belong among the most awesome symbols of eternity.

The best time to see the mountains of the West is at daybreak, not from within their shadow but from a point somewhere far out on the high plain. At first they seem to flow away into the distance in an unbroken mass, but as the dawn brightens they assume individual identity, separate into enormous hunch-backed figures, forever marching and forever fixed, that dwarf into nothingness all things that live; and the great plain in its uncomplicated immensity absorbs all traces of man's being. It is then, in the strange half-light of coming dawn, that the mountains and the plain assume a grandeur and immutability that compel the beholder, however arrogant he may be in the light of common day, to recognize his own insignificance.

I have often thought that the high plain and mountain country of Alberta is no place for an ambitious man. In the city you can build up and tear down skyscrapers and feel yourself a god; but no man can move a mountain or make more than a few scratches, soon to be obliterated, on the limitless surface of the plain.

The green mountain streams rush helter-skelter over rock and shale to join the waters of the Bow River — so to be borne east through the wide mountain valley and across the great plains into Lake Winnipeg and thence by the Nelson River into arctic seas. But the Highway points us in the opposite direction, towards the Great Divide, the height of land rising less than five miles beyond Lake Louise. Soon the land will fall away imperceptibly to the west and all the great rivers, no matter how wild and far their wanderings, flow at last into the Pacific.

Prairie

Peter Stevens

There is nothing

nothing to stand in
the way of the eye.

Earth rolls under light
scabbed by brush.

Over water course
over slough and sand-flat

eye travels out
to rest on land's ledge.

Sky sheets down
sun-glazed air

eye open
in/to space where

there is nothing.

Kitsalano

Alexander M. Stephen

Kitsalano, on the dark waters,
  Drifting out in waves that run
Softly through the crimson twilight
  To the gateway of the sun,
I have felt your spirit moving,
  Where the evening shadows throng,
I have heard your many voices
  Stir and tremble into song.

Where the miles of fragrant cedar
  And the dark firs whisper low
To the curving line of silver
  Where the moonlit waters flow,
There are ghostly echoes surging
  In the sea wind borne afar
From the hidden lands of slumber
  Out beyond the western star.

Where the long canoe crept swiftly
  Like a panther on its foe,
Now the stately liner glitters
  And the great winged vessels go.
Where you hunters passed in silence
  Like a gull on flashing wings,
Now the turbines churn and grumble
  And the long smoke trails and swings.

Clear, above the ghostly echoes,
  Strong, beyond the traders' din,
Kitsalano, Spirit calling,
  I have heard your music thin
Weave a magic web of beauty
  In the dusk that folds the world.

In the crimson flower of sunset,
I have seen your glory furled.

Smile when dusty savants point us
To the past's dim-scented page.
Pity those who see no wonder
In the dawn-red of an age.
Beauty still is at the portal
And a word shall be the key
Opening doors to treasure buried
Here beside our ancient sea.

Kitsalano, in the twilight,
Link your stars into a chain.
Place our feet upon your pathway.
Show us love beyond our pain.
Gleaming hills and distant valleys
Still are trembling with your fire.
On the dark horizon resting,
Show us peaks of new desire.

Gibsons is Gone

Ken Sudhues

sitting, waiting,
seeing only a pane
and my reflection.

(the fog rolled in.
the village across the bay disappeared)

boats and voices meander,
probing through
the wall of white
to their moorings.

streetlights appear, green
stars on grey-black
nothing.

the creamer and fruit bowl
sit there; existing
the butter dish is in limbo.

snow-crowned Grantham's Hill
looms, out of perspective.
I see glowing Christmas lights.
and now the flashing B. of M. sign.

sometimes greyly-blue sections
of the village appear from their
palls of mist.

others lie enshrouded.

it is late. people turn off
their lights. They blink out until
tomorrow dusk.
here comes a new assault by the white banks.

from the east comes the fog.
Grantham's disappears.
B. of M. is gone.
the Shell and Esso signs.
all the pretty Christmas lights
Gibsons is gone.

sitting, waiting
seeing only a pane,
and my reflection.

Pacific Edge

Patrick Lane

Between great stones
the sea rises
up
  down
    turning on
itself fighting
streamers of weed
of moon phosphorescent
glow on foam light
on twisted branch
where a crab
hangs washing
up
  down
    turning on
itself fighting
the sea

The Mysterious North

Pierre Berton

. . . I was brought up in a small frame cottage in Dawson City, where the walls were a foot thick and filled with sawdust to keep out the cold, where a pot of dog food — rice and caribou meat — bubbled perpetually over a wood fire, and where the water was brought around to the door in icicle-draped buckets at twenty-five cents a pail.

Our home lay nestled against the low benchland that skirts the swampy flats beside the gray Yukon River. Behind us rose the black bulk of the hills, clothed in spruce and birch and poplar. Behind those hills lay other hills, and when you climbed to the top of the farthest hills, there were yet more hills stretching endlessly into the north. If a man wanted to walk in a straight line due north he could cross those hills for four hundred miles until he reached the edge of the Arctic sea, and he would come upon no trace of human life.

I have never quite been able to escape the memory of those lonely hills. In the winter nights, when the roar of the river was hushed by a mantle of ice, when the frost-racked timbers cracked like pistol-shots in the cold, when the ghostly bars of the northern lights shifted across the black sky, we would sometimes hear the chill call of the wolf, drifting down from the wilderness behind us. It is an eerie sound, plaintive, mournful, mysterious. The wolf is like the husky and the malemute: his vocal cords are so constructed that he cannot bark, but only howl across the endless hills. If the north has a theme song, it is this haunting cry, which seems to echo all the loneliness and the wonder of the land at the top of the continent.

When I was a small boy, it used to fascinate and terrify me, perhaps because in all my years in the north I never actually saw a wolf alive. To me he was only a footprint in the snow and a sound in the night, an unseen creature who lurked in the shadow of the nameless hills.

For eleven childhood winters I heard the cry of the wolf, and then I left the country with no intention of returning. But the north has dogged my footsteps and I have never quite been quit of it. Within five years I was back again on the aspen-covered slopes of the Klondike, working with a pick and shovel in a gold camp. I spent three summers at it and then, when war broke out I left it again, believing that this was the end. It was only the beginning: since those days in the Yukon I have crisscrossed the north from the Alaska border to the tip of Baffin Island, from Churchill on Hudson Bay to Coppermine on the

Arctic coast. I have eaten moose steak on the Peace River, buffalo meat in Fort Smith, Arctic grayling in Whitehorse, and reindeerburgers in Aklavik. I have driven the Alaska highway in a Ford, landed in Headless Valley in a Junkers, crossed Great Slave Lake in a tugboat, and chugged into the heart of Labrador on an ore train . . .

The more I see of the country, the less I feel I know about it. There is a saying that after five years in the north every man is an expert; after ten years, a novice. No man can hope or expect to absorb it all in a lifetime, and fifteen generations of explorers, whalers, fur traders, missionaries, scientists, policemen, trappers, prospectors, adventurers, and tourists have failed to solve all its riddles. To me as to most northerners, the country is still an unknown quantity, as elusive as the wolf, howling just beyond the rim of the hills. Perhaps that is why it holds its fascination . . .

The high Arctic, which knows no real summer, bears little relation to the Yukon Valley of my childhood, where the temperatures can rise to a hundred degrees. The treeless tundra northwest of Churchill, Manitoba, where century-old trees grow no higher than three inches, has little in common with the Mackenzie farmlands, where a stem of wheat can sprout five feet in a month. The stark, Precambrian rock on which Port Radium is perched is a long way removed from the spongy delta in which Aklavik is mired.

For the north is a land of violent contrasts. It has some of the most breath-taking scenery in the world. There is the unforgettable picture of Baffin Island rearing out of the Arctic mists, with its black cliffs and its blue mountains and its long fiords and its enormous emerald glaciers. There is the site of Kluane Lake in the Yukon as you first come upon it from the Alaska Highway, a slender finger of the purest absinthe green, lying lazily at the foot of the continent's tallest mountain range, whose peaks plunge in purple slabs straight out of the clouds to the water's edge. There is the breathless spectacle of the Nahanni Valley with its enormous waterfall locked away beyond a series of dizzy, precipitous canyons.

But the north also contains some of the most desolate and monotonous stretches in the world. Dismal Lake, "a sombre sheet of water between threatening hills" north of Great Bear, is truly named. "Anything more unspeakably dismal than the western end I never saw," the traveler George Douglas was moved to remark. Another explorer, Henry Youle Hind, stood on the tableland above the Moisie River in Labrador and wrote that "words fail to describe the appalling desolation." Hesketh Prichard wrote that the Ungava Peninsula was "sheer desolation — abysmal and chaotic".

Indeed, there is so much monotony in the north that its very vastness takes on a sort of grandeur, like the Barren Lands that stretch across the top of the continent for hundreds of miles, their starkness broken only by those geological oddities with the elfin names: the pingoes and the polygons, the drumlins and the eskers.

The Canadian north contains more lakes than all the rest of the world put together, all the way from little green-eyed Muncho on the Alaska Highway, to Great Bear, the continent's fourth largest, so cold that it often stays frozen until July. But it also encompasses one of the world's great deserts, the Arctic tundra, where the precipitation runs between two and ten inches yearly. The fact that thousands of lakes happen to lie in this desert country makes it all the more confusing.

The north is full of such paradoxes. In fact, it is possible to prove just about any theory by the use of isolated examples and statistics.

Is it a frozen waste? There are plenty of places where Eskimos wear fur-lined parkas the year around, where planes land on skis in June and the temperature never goes higher than fifteen degrees above frost.

Is it a sunny paradise? At Fort Smith, on the Slave River,

the thermometer has sometimes reached 103 degrees above zero. This is hotter than has ever been recorded in Canada's southernmost city, Windsor, Ontario. Spring comes to Norman Wells, nudging the Arctic Circle, just as soon as it does to the Gaspe Peninsula in Quebec. The average July temperatures in Dawson City are the same as those on the central prairies. And the radio station at Resolution Island, off the coast of Baffin, has an average temperature in January slightly higher than the average for Winnipeg, eight hundred miles to the south. In fact, slightly colder temperatures have been recorded in the northern prairie provinces than have ever been recorded in Arctic Canada.

The truth, of course, is that the north is neither paradise nor wasteland. It remains a frontier country, with only two important resources, fur and minerals. (A third great resource, hydroelectric power, has yet to be developed.) It is still desperately remote and costly to reach and exploit, but it is capable of supporting if necessary (but only if necessary) a much larger population than it now enjoys. . . .

There remains one serious flaw in the northern economy: almost every community is built on a single resource. When the bottom falls out of gold, Yellowknife suffers a slump. When the bottom drops out of furs, the Mackenzie River ports face a depression. John Hornby, a bizarre and mystic little Englishman who roamed the Barrens for a generation, called that country "the land of feast and famine". He wanted to write a book with that title, but he starved to death before he began it. The phrase remains an apt one and it could well apply to the north as a whole.

It is this boom and bust psychology that has given the north a certain feeling and look of impermanence. Nobody expects to stay very long in the north — or very long in one spot. There is no agriculture to tie people to a single site. Like the caribou and the lemmings and the nomadic Indians, northerners are apt to rove the land like gypsies. The Anglican missionaries, the

Hudson's Bay traders and the Mounted Policemen are switched from post to post like chessmen on a great board. The prospectors follow the big strikes, and the trappers follow the fur. This restless shifting gives the north a cohesion it otherwise would not have. Northerners know each other, even though a thousand miles separate their homes; men living in Whitehorse, Yukon, are bound to have acquaintances in Aklavik, Yellowknife, and Churchill. But it also contributes to the feeling, strong in every northern town, that everything is temporary. Many northern communities (Whitehorse is one example) are little better than shack towns for this reason. The homes are jerry-built and so are the buildings, and often enough they are sprinkled around the countryside without thought or plan as if tossed there by the passing winds.

The fact is that most people go north expecting to stay only a short while. And yet the country is populated by men and women (my parents were among them) who have stayed a lifetime. I can never forget the story of the young Scottish bride who came to Dawson City in the days before the First World War. She brought a trunk of wedding presents with her, but she didn't bother to unpack them, for she didn't expect to stay more than a few months. But the months grew into years, and the years grew into decades. She raised a family and watched them grow up. She learned to live with the north and love it. The crisp feeling of the snow crust breaking under the moccasin in the winter, the bright tangle of kinnikinnick carpeting the forest floor in the summer, the exploding rumble of ice breaking in the spring, the pungent odor of caribou rotting along the riverbank in the fall — all these sensations and impressions became a part of her life. Finally the time came for her to leave the north however, and when she did, it was with that strange mixture of relief and reluctance that every northerner faces when the day of departure comes. She packed her trunks and went her way, but one trunk was already full. For here lay the still unopened wedding presents of thirty years before, the telltale symbols of her indecision about a land which, in all its mystery, both bewitches and repels — like the gossamer fog of winter clothing the dark valleys, or the chill call of the wolf drifting down from the unending hills.

Sunrise North

Elizabeth Brewster

Drawing my drapes, I see
pink and purple clouds of dawn
over the white-roofed city,
smoke in rising fountains,
the lights of early risers
twinkling far off.
the new moon, hanging low,
beginning to pale in the morning sky.

The beautiful northern city
is a child's Christmas toy
spread out like blocks
with here and there a tree
deftly placed
discreetly frosted,
and, like a child,
I want to pick it up.
move a house here a tree there
put more frost on that distant dome.

A Young Farmer

James M. Moir

The days stretch out
endless with toil.

The hard land
thrusts him along
his inevitable way.

Enclosed in lonely spaces
of earth and sky
he seeks his to-morrow.

With darkness in his blood
he lies in darkness
at the day's end,

hearing the wind sigh
over miles of prairie.

Prairie at Evening

Wilfrid Eggleston

Down sinks the sun;
Down falls the wind;
Down cools the lonely plain;
Up surges all the charm of night:
The scent of stocks, the fading light,
The nightjar, and the rustling grain . . .

And now the dreamer's eyes may see
Beyond the shadow-haunted plain
The hills, still golden in the sun
Where glamor lurks, and poetry
Will rise when day's dull prose is done.

Field in the Wind

Floris McLaren

The grass is running in the wind
Without a sound,
Crouching and smooth and fast
Along the ground.
The clouds run too,
And little shadows play
And scurry in the grass
That will not stay,
But runs and runs, until
The wind is still.

Telephone Poles

Betty Dyck

Four-armed sentinels
Stretching forth their tireless limbs,
Silhouetted silently
In the Prairie sunset.
Hugging the highway,
Hinged with humming wires
Vibrant whispers whistling
Through the quiet countryside —
Extensions of the larynx.
Who calls?
The voice of a nation.
Who answers?
All.

The Gopher

Myra Smith Stilborn

I am not taken in by the innocent guise
Of that firm little figure erect on a mound;
Though he pose as an artist of shrill whistled cries,
I am not taken in. By the innocent guise
You would scarcely suspect him as one of the spies
Of a wheat-thieving gang from the haunts underground.
I am not taken in by the innocent guise
Of that bold little bandit erect on a mound.

The Prairies

Marjorie Dingwall

If you've ever lived on the prairies
They will never let you go,
There is something about the prairies
Only prairie people know;
A fragrance, a faint wind stirring,
A sunset sky aglow,
If you've ever lived on the prairies
They will never let you go.

If you've ever lived on the prairies
You will not settle down,
Amid the peace and beauty
Of a pleasant seaside town.
For the sun swept waves of the prairie grass
Where the shadows smile and frown,
Will beckon and call you back again
And you will not settle down.

If you've ever lived on the prairies

There are many things you'll know —
Blue skies, wild flowers in springtime,
Indian Summer's golden glow;
The quiet of the evening
When the light of day is low.
If you've ever lived on the prairies
They will never let you go.

My Prairies

Miriam Mandel

I left the edge of our small city
when I was very small.
There was a stream
which seemed big
but I didn't get very wet.

I climbed a small hill
to the open prairies
which was
really
a deserted golf course.
My eyes widened
in delight
at the sight
of prairies I had never seen.

On my knees
I found
yellow buffalo beans
purple crocuses
the white grace
of Queen Anne's lace
and something else white
that smelled very sweet.

There were cactuses
sown so tight to the ground
I couldn't loosen
their red, yellow and orange
blooms.

I gathered my flowers
rushed home to mother
to present her
with my gift.

Her face went grey
with fear
when I told her where
I'd been.
But I went again and again
to see
the blooming prairies.

Prairie Impression

Margot Osborn

The world is a silver penny
Impossibly large
And I am in the middle of it,
A penny reaching from rim to dull grey rim of sky
That curves above my head, a lustreless bowl.
There is nothing but the snow and I.
The snow in shadowed hummocks is its superscription
But I cannot read the language nor make out the design.
I am alone in this white desolation.
Though I move, it travels with me,
Featureless,
And I still remain in the middle.

Prairie Season

Marci Gamble

The acrid smell of burning grasses,
Shafts of stubble in islands of black,
Brown stalks of last year's sunflower plants.
Wet spring, dry spring — wheat crop, barley crop.
This is April on the Prairies.

Blowing soil, green shoots, machinery time,
"Last year we got 8 inches of snow the end of April."
"Got your seed cleaned yet? My tractor blew a gasket."
Wet spring, dry spring — rapeseed or barley
This is May on the Prairies.

Warm sun, long hours, oil fumes, honest sweat,
"This year we'll spray for wild oats. Fertilizer sure
  costs."
"Thought I'd grow as much wheat as possible, rest in
  rape."
Wet spring, dry spring — liquid fertilizer, herbicide,
This is June on the Prairies.

Haying Time, 1953

Barbara Sapergia

the men are working in the shop
an old rusty boxcar dark inside
hot   full of grease, junk, boards
spare parts, nameless equipment

                    little breezes
raise circles of dust in the yard
shiver the caragana leaves

in the kitchen
you can hear the clock ticking
the old cookstove simmering
soup from fresh green peas
it's almost time

i look at the shop welding lights
play like bright stars you are not
supposed to look without a mask
you will go blind i look nothing
moves there is no sound not even
the sound of machines only wind
the caragana leaves are yellowing

grandma nods i run to the well
draw up a long rope & a quart sealer
i hear her calling the men
"hey — come on! dinner!" she whistles
her sweet piercing whistle
i can never figure out
how she does that

i beat uncle ben back to the house
we make the screen door slam
his face is red & seamed with
white rings from his mask
he shakes his head
"ninety above &
the tractor breaks down"
he pours water in the basin
splashes his face & cool
crystal drops hover in the air
he dries with a soft old towel
the water makes his face
look smooth & young again

i hand him the sealer
slippery with a fine chill mist

with both hands he tips it
gulping the icy liquid
sweet/sour buttery bits
his hot breath becomes
clouds in the jar

Prairie Gold

R. E. Rashley

Here where the field was green a month ago
The thresher squats among the stooks and purrs
With deep content while sheaf-racks come and go
And forks ply eager in a sun that spurs
Bronzed backs to fierce endeavour. On the road
The dust haze hangs all day where trucks freight in
Their heavy prairie gleaning. Load by load
The red grain piles up brightly in the bin.

No mine is rich as these broad fields alive
With harvestry; no mineral as rare
As this red furrow ore which soon will pour
Down iron ways to glut great ports and drive
Across three seas to half the world and more
With summer's wealth and nature's elixir.

Harvest Time

E. Pauline Johnson

Pillowed and hushed on the silent plain,
Wrapped in her mantle of golden grain,

Wearied of pleasuring weeks away,
Summer is lying asleep to-day, —

Where winds come sweet from the wild-rose briers
And the smoke of the far-off prairie fires.

Yellow her hair as the goldenrod,
And brown her cheeks as the prairie sod;

Purple her eyes as the mists that dream
At the edge of some laggard sun-drowned stream;

But over their depths the lashes sweep,
For Summer is lying to-day asleep.

The north wind kisses her rosy mouth,
His rival frowns in the far-off south,

And comes caressing her sunburnt cheek,
And Summer awakes for one short week, —

Awakes and gathers her wealth of grain,
Then sleeps and dreams for a year again.

The Golden Time

Sharleen M. Chevraux

Frantic, frustrating, fulfilling! It's harvest time again.

I am that not-so-rare creature called a town girl who married a farmer without knowing anything about farm life — its joys or its hardships. And many facets of the life still remain outside my ken. I have not yet mastered the mysteries of harrowing *versus* cultivating, rodweeding or discing. But I have learned perhaps the most important fact of all. The deep, soul-satisfying significance of harvest.

There is a growing excitement as the hot summer days of August complete the maturation of the crops — wheat, barley and rape on our farm. The men become tense, excited, a bit edgy. The combines and swathers are pulled out of the shed to be serviced, repaired, checked. Nothing must break down during the few short weeks that harvest is possible.

Evenings are spent tramping the fields, watching for signs that the grain is ready for the swather. Suddenly the time seems long — too long to wait; and short — too short to get everything ready. Then the evening finally comes. "That barley field will be ready by Tuesday."

Only two more days to go. Last minute repairs — a furious rush for parts that have been ordered but haven't arrived. A sudden discovery. "That belt looks like it won't last through harvest. Better get another just in case."

Weather reports become all important. I've learned that one major duty of farm wives at this time is to listen to weather reports, read weather reports and watch weather reports as often as they are available.

Monday night. Rain is forecast. An anxious evening — half hoping that rain will fall (it could help fill the heads of those crops not yet ready), and half hoping it won't so the men can get started.

Tuesday morning. No rain but a heavy dew. Swathing is delayed until noon. The tempo of work picks up but won't reach its height until the combines are also working, several days later.

At last all the machinery rolls and harvest is really here. Now there is a never-ending list of things for wives to do. Make meals. Pack lunches. Fill water jugs. Take grain samples to town to be tested. Snatch a few minutes to ride the combine or the truck hauling the grain to bins.

Back to the meals again.

Meals. That is one of the best of all times at harvest. Dinner in the field, served hot and eaten picnic style among the swathes in the shade of a combine.

Making the meals is no problem, but packing them and keeping them hot is. Boxes and jars, wax paper and foil wrap are laid out. Spill proof salt and pepper shakers, sealed dishes of butter, small, individual packages of bread, dishes and cutlery — all assembled and packed. Then comes the food. Lots of it.

More than we would normally eat in two weeks, but harvesting is hungry work and so is watching it. Perhaps it is roast today with potatoes and gravy, two kinds of vegetables, and pie for dessert. Or maybe fried chicken, or hamburger, or sausages. Maybe a baked pudding or cake and fruit. Into the boxes it goes. Now we're ready. Oops! Forgot the tea or the coffee or the milk or the Kool-aid. Everyone of us has his or her own preference. The jars are filled, packed, and we're away.

Children clamber into the car or the truck, with careful instructions not to put their feet in the dinner, and we set out to find the men. Normally I know the field they're in but sometimes they fool me. They've moved and I have to search until I find them.

Even when we reach the field, it is such a maze of corners, bush patches and sloughs that it may take some time before I actually spot the combines — one on one side of the field and one on the other. Nothing to do but choose a spot half way between and begin laying out the food while the combines make their ponderous way in my direction — feeding on the broad swathes with a continuous, fascinating hunger as they come.

The trucks arrive and soon a group of dusty people are gathered — sprawling against the swathes, leaning on the combines or trucks — all with heaping plates and healthy appetites. It is peaceful, serene. The sun burns and shimmers while a slight breeze fans us gently — just enough to keep the wasps, attracted by the smell of food, from settling down. An indistinct hum of insects — a few bird songs and silence. Conversation is sparse and lazy. For a few minutes there is no need for hurry or noise.

Those short periods of comradeship, of golden peace, can be compared to few other moments in life. There is a satisfaction, a love, a warm oneness with nature that is rare in our world of hustle-bustle. But they end too soon.

The hungry giants snort back to life and begin again their gorging. The trucks race to keep up — filling and unfilling their boxes with golden grain. I hasten to pick up the remains of dinner, repack the dishes and head for home. If I am quick enough I will have enough time to ride the combine or act as a truck "swamper" for awhile before supper and lunches need to be made.

There is an excitement composed of dust, heat, hurry and monotony that goes with harvest. The haulers sit for long, slow minutes waiting for the grain hoppers to fill. Then they must speed to the combines, driving with precision and care while the grain spews forth, waiting for the honk which means "hopper empty". A rush to the bins and a quick trip back. A new load and long, slow minutes of waiting. The combines go round and round in an ever diminishing circuit, only to move and begin again.

But harvest is more than these things. It is watching the swathes disappear; watching the bins fill. It is listening for combines in the late evening; watching isolated lights move slowly across a darkened field. It is running outside to feel the grass and know how much longer the men can work. It is satisfaction and fulfillment. The crops are in. One year's work is safely done.

Lightning Storm

Sid Marty

The forestry line is shorted out
has been for weeks
Picking up the ear piece
we hear
a thousand birds on a wire
miles apart
each in separate song
I don't know how this can be
While somewhere a lynx growls

from a lodgepole pine
where a bird was singing
on an insulator

During the lightning storm
the bell rings slowly
on every strike
resistors smoke
the line to Jasper is out
The district warden's 30 miles up
the Little Cairn river
hasn't been heard from
can't be reached

Twelve spruce have fallen
on the lines at Beaver Cabin
In the morning, we'll be climbing
splicing wire, cutting deadfalls
with the chainsaw

Answering the switchboard's ring
I shout, "do you need help?"
Far away the faint voice
fades in the sound of lightning
sound of wild cats in the timber

Moraine Lake

R. H. Blackburn

There is no time here. These are cinders of it
Spilled from the forges of the gods of thunder
Who, with their ringing hammers striking fire,
Beat out the rock that still was hot with time,
But now there is no time; the noiseless shadows
Of yesterday sweep from the snow-fast peaks
To clasp hands with the shadows of tomorrow

Across the ice-blue water of the ages,
And all are one, for time is long burned out.
Man, who has made a dial and called it time,
Finds the word useless here, as if he held
A candle to the sun, for here the gods
Have built a Babel where all tongues are one
In the still, timeless language of the heart.

The Wild

Jody McCurdy

The wilderness
Wild,
As the wind
Blowing endlessly

Deserted,
Seemingly untouched
By time

Holding
Beauty, mystery
In its
Arms

Sunrise on Lake Louise

Ella Elizabeth Clark

Long, long ago, when the world was very young, giants lived in this country. A chief of the giants was a famous hunter. Many large game animals he killed with his bow and arrows. Many birds and small game animals he caught in his traps. But he was never satisfied; always he wanted more.

One day, as he stood watching a rainbow, he had an idea: he

would get the rainbow and from it he would make a giant bow for hunting. The more he watched, the more he wanted the rainbow. With it he could be a truly great hunter.

So he climbed the tallest tree on the highest mountain, reached up to the sky with his long arms, and tore the rainbow from its place. But when he seized it, the colours disappeared. The bow in his hands was colourless.

Angrily the giant threw the rainbow against the nearest mountain-top, a peak overlooking a lake. There the bow broke into pieces and the pieces rolled on down into the water. At the bottom of the lake the fragments regained their colours, and the colours spread through the water.

After awhile the spirit-power in the sky made the smaller bow which we still see after a rain. Sometimes, even today, the colours of the rainbow which was shattered by the giant-chief may be seen at sunrise in the water of the lake we now call Lake Louise.

Lake Minnewanka

Ella Elizabeth Clark

Northeast of Lake Minnewanka is a mountain with a high, sharp peak shaped like a tower. From a long distance you can see snow on its top, but there is never any on its side. The mountain is so steep that snow does not stay on it. Because spirits lived on top of it, Indians called it Spirit Mountain.

The near-by lake they called "Minnewanka", which means "Water of the Spirits". Whenever they travelled in the neighbourhood of the lake, they heard voices of the spirits. As they passed by, they could see nothing that made sounds, but they could hear sounds.

One time when our people were camping near the lake, my father heard what seemed to be the beating of a drum. The noise seemed to be coming from the water. He could also hear voices down in the lake. Soon he noticed that water was coming up on the shore. It came close to the camp, and then it went back again.

Soon my father saw, near the centre of the lake, a strange creature rise out of the water. It was half fish and half human being. It had blown the water toward the shore, and then it had come above the surface. As my father stood watching, the fish-person sank back into the lake.

Other people also saw the strange creature. They were so frightened that they broke camp and never camped there again. All Indians stayed away from that water. There was no fishing or canoeing on Lake Minnewanka until white people came.

Strange creatures in other lakes were sometimes killed by lightning, but I never heard of this one being killed.

Many Indians are still afraid of the lake. A few years ago some Indian boys were working there, helping to build a dam. They did not want to work at that place, because they had heard about the strange fish person. One of the boys was killed in a strange accident. Some of the people say that the accident happened because the spirits did not like to have the trees near the lake destroyed.

At Crow's Nest Pass

E. Pauline Johnson

At Crow's Nest Pass the mountains rend
Themselves apart, the rivers wend
  A lawless course about their feet,
  And breaking into torrents beat
In useless fury where they blend
    At Crow's Nest Pass.

The nesting eagle, wise, discreet,
Wings up the gorge's lone retreat
And makes some barren crag her friend
At Crow's Nest Pass.

Uncertain clouds, half-high, suspend
Their shifting vapours, and contend
With rocks that suffer not defeat;
And snows, and suns, and mad winds meet
To battle where the cliffs defend
At Crow's Nest Pass.

A Mountain Journey

Howard O'Hagan

Dave Conroy, whose breath had hung stubby icicles on his moustache, paused upon the very summit of the pass. He tucked his ski poles under his arms, leaned upon them, sinking their discs into the creaking snow, and while he rested there panting, the cold was an old man's fingers feeling craftily through his clothes.

He was tired. He was so tired that his mouth was dry with the taste of salt. He was more tired than he had any right to be, and Hoodoo cabin on Hoodoo creek, where he could pass the night, was still five miles away. It was downhill now though, downhill all the way. For the first time during the long day he could stand back on his skis and let them carry him where he wished to go. Since daylight he had come twenty miles and climbed four thousand feet from the lower Smokey to the pass. On his shoulders he had lifted upwards with him at every step his pack of food for another five days on the trail, his blankets, axe and fifty pounds of fur for the market — the result of six weeks' trapping on the head of the Jackpine. At every step too, he had broken trail and his skis had sunk a foot in the new snow, white and soft as flour.

He knew as he stood on the summit that he should have made camp two miles back in the timber and crossed the divide in the morning. Back there he had passed a fine spruce tree, its wide branches sweeping low, so that close against its trunk, cradled in its roots, he had seen the brown mossy ground where no snow had fallen and where he might have made his fire and spread his blankets. That tree, like a strong and lonely woman, called to his weary body to stop. But two hours of daylight remained and he went on.

He thought that if he had waited another two weeks to come out, till March, the snow would have had a crust for travelling, the days would have been longer, the cold less severe. Anyway, a man was a fool to travel alone in the mountains, especially with a heavy pack, bucking a fresh fall of snow. A man when he was alone would travel too far. He would travel till he could travel no more, for the mere sake of travelling, when a day or two's delay in the time of his arrival made no difference at all.

Still, the worst was over. It was downgrade now to the railroad, eighty miles of trail along the Snake Indian river with cabins to put up at every night. No more siwashing under trees, burrowing four feet down in the snow for a place to sleep, with a snow-covered tree sweating in the heat of his fire, dripping water on his neck and dampening his blankets. Not that under such conditions a man slept very much. It was too cold. If he slept, his fire slept with him. It was better to stay awake, his blankets over his shoulders, and a pile of wood handy at his elbow.

Up there on the pass it was very still. No wind blew and his breath rose white and yellow before him. His heart thumped and hissed in his breast, and the silence about him as he listened became a roar as if it were the roar of the grey earth rolling on through space and time. Behind him his ski trail stretched a few feet, two black lines with the webbed marks of his ski poles pacing beside them. Mist, like the shadow of universal darkness on the treeless summit, moved about him, searched every crevice of the mountain land, roamed in great billows, formed in the blindness and suffering of eternal homelessness.

Conroy turned his skis down the slope before him. He was beginning to feel like a ghost on an abandoned planet and he wanted to see the works of man about him once again. He longed for the sight of a cabin, a clearing in the forest, yellow flaming blazes on trees beside the trail. Snow, flung up by the prow of his skis, pattered lightly against his thighs and as he hummed downwards he thought of supper — brown curled bacon, brown bannock, rice with butter melting on it, tea red and strong as rum.

The rolling alplands, a white sea frozen into weary immobility, became a broken parkland and he made long sweeping turns around clumps of spruce and balsam. Dark green trees came out of the thinning mist towards him, touched him with outflung branches, passed in a flutter and flurry of snowdust. The cold wind against his face, the loud wind howling in crescendo by his ears, the flow of wind that pressed his trousers tight against his legs, gave him back strength as he exulted in the rush of his descent. Tears smarted in his eyes and through them he saw the landscape opaque and blurred as though it were vibrating to the speed of his passage.

He swung to the right in a wide telemark that threw snow in his face, swept down an open meadowland where the black tips of willows showed between two walls of timber, dropped off a cutbank to the frozen river, glanced a moment over his shoulder at the curved beauty of his ski trail on the hill above, curved and smooth and thin, like the tracing of a pen upon the snow.

And as he looked back, while still sliding forward with the momentum of his descent, the ice broke beneath him. It broke with a low muffled reverberation, startling as if the river had spoken. The snow rifted about him, the points of his skis dropped down. He was thrown forward and to save himself from falling on his face plunged down his hands. His pack slipped forward upon the back of his head and held him. The river was shallow and his hands rested on its gravelled bottom. He saw the snow melt around his wrists and flow into the top of his mittens, searing the flesh of his wrists like flame. He saw dark water streaming in furrows by his wrists and before he staggered upright again heard water tinkling over pebbles, murmuring, protesting, running downhill between ice and pebbles to the Arctic Ocean.

Conroy was too weak to rise beneath the pack. He rolled over upon his side, slipped the thongs of the ski poles from his wrists, dropped his pack on the snow beside him, raised himself and lifted his skis from the water. Water had seeped down his socks into his boots and his feet were cold and clammy.

He had fallen into an air hole. Probably a warm spring entered into the river nearby and above it the ice was thin. That was a peril of winter travel. But the rivers, levelled with ice and snow, were the winter highways of the mountains, and a man, when he could, travelled along them in preference to breaking a heavy trail in the timber.

Conroy unclamped his skis, upended them, and stood knee deep in the snow. Already the water on them had crusted into ice. He took off his sodden mittens, opened his clasp-knife, and tried to scrape the ice from the skis' running surface. He knew what he should do. He should stop, make a fire, dry his hands and feet, change his socks and mittens. But it was late. It would mean siwashing for another night underneath a tree. A biting wind was driving the mist back up the valley and the sun westering behind the ranges threw long feeble shadows across the snow. He was less than three miles from the cabin, and the promise of its warmth and comfort would not let him stop.

He wriggled his toes in his boots. They were cold, but perhaps, he thought, not wet. Only his ankles and heels seemed wet. If he hurried he could make it. He slammed his right foot back into his ski iron, bent down to clamp it to his ski, but his fingers already were numbed with the cold. He rose again, thrashed his arms about his shoulders, bringing the blood tingling to their tips, opened his packsack and found a pair of woollen inner mitts. He would have to get along without the moose-hide outers. They were already frozen stiff and he put them into his pack.

His skis clamped to his feet at last, he hoisted his pack, took his poles and started off, hunching his toes to keep the circulation going. Ice on the bottom of the skis dragged heavily in the snow, but he fought against it, pushing on his poles, knowing that speed was his one means of escape from the cold hand of wilderness that pressed against his back.

The long white avenue of the river opened before him, lined on either side by tall spruce trees. The wind was rising with the sundown. It whipped snow against his face, cut through the weave of his woollen mitts, set the forest moaning beside him. He bent his head against it, his eyes on the black tapering points of his skis, ducking and dodging through the snow. It was as though he were engaged in some fantastic pursuit with those ski points always just beyond him, their tight cheeks pulled back into a cadaverous grin.

His shoulder muscles, as he lunged against the ski poles, bulged as though they would burst their skin, ached until their pain became a cry within him. His legs moving back and forth beneath him seemed tireless. They could go on forever and he no longer knew whether he could stop them. The pain in his shoulders was the only reality of his existence and his body was no more than the shape of agony and effort crawling through the twilight, across the long shadows of spruce trees laid upon the snow.

He came up from the river through the timber into the cabin clearing. But no log walls rose to greet him. No closed door waited for his touch to open. He stood in the middle of the clearing where the cabin had been, hemmed about by swaying pine trees, pine trees that swayed as the wind sighed through them. Snow, as if it had garnered light from the day, cast upwards a shadowless glow and Conroy saw close to him the black butts of congregated logs, a corner of the cabin, draped in white, rising lonely as a monument left by men a hundred years ago.

Since he had passed that way, fire had gutted the cabin. A few log ends remained above ground. It was as though the cabin had subsided into the snow that rose like a slow inundation to cover it. A beggared moon from behind a grey rack of clouds wandered in the sky above the earth's desolation and in its light he perceived on the slope above him, where the fire had leaped from the cabin, stiff, branchless trees, like a parade of skeletons climbing up the mountainside.

The next cabin was at Blue creek, eighteen miles down the river. It was farther than he had strength to go. He would camp here in the clearing where the cabin had been burned. He slipped his pack off and reached toward it for the handle of his axe to cut kindling, making shavings for his fire. His fingers refused to bend. Protected only by the woollen mitts, they were stiff with the cold. He beat his hands about his shoulders, flung his arms in circles, took off his mittens and rubbed his hands together in the snow, but felt no blood pulsing in his fingertips.

He bit his fingers. They were cold and white and unresponsive as a dead man's. His right thumb tingled; when he rubbed his hands across his face, his beard bristled on the palms. It was only his fingers that defied him. He had been a fool. He should have made a fire when he fell through the ice, and should have spent the night three miles up the river under a tree. He had always said that mountain travel was not dangerous if a man knew how to take care of himself. Any man who froze his hands or feet had only himself to blame.

As he stood there, stamping on his skis, his arms flapping at his sides, he remembered Duncan Macdonald, who trapped in the Beaver river country and who had walked thirty miles to the railroad on frozen feet to have them amputated by the doctor. Because he could trap no more, Macdonald had opened a cobbler's shop in Jasper to make boots he could no longer wear himself, and Conroy saw him now at his bench, laughing, not saying anything at all, just laughing, his red face wrinkled as he nodded his heavy bald head and laughed.

Conroy decided that his hands were not frozen, his feet, which he could no longer feel in his boots, not frozen. They were only numb. He needed fire to warm them. Since he could not make kindling, since he could not bend his fingers around the shaft of his axe, he would set a tree afire, he would set the forest in a blaze around him and warm himself in its midst. Small dry twigs under a spruce tree would flame like paper. Putting his left wrist over his right, he forced his right hand into the pocket where he carried his match-safe. He pried it out and it fell into the snow at his feet. He spread his skis and leaned down to pick it up. He poked his hands into the snow. They were like two sticks of wood on the ends of his arms and shoved the safe deeper and farther from him. He stooped lower still and finally, pressing it between his wrists, filched it out. He held it there before him, at arm's length, a round tin cylinder that contained the red flame and blustering smoke of fire. His right thumb, still moving to his command, pressed it into his palm, but his fingers would not catch it, would not twist it open. They would not bring the match-safe to him. They held it from him. If they would only bend, those fingers. If they would understand when he spoke to them.

He looked about him as if he would find the realities of his situation in the snow at his feet. He was eighty miles from the railroad, a journey of four days. Unable to light a fire, without warmth or food, he would never make it. His fingers were frozen. His feet probably were frozen too. He had one chance. Across the river from Hoodoo creek where he stood, a high pass led over into the Moose river. Frank MacMoran trapped up there and had his cabin on Terrace creek. From Hoodoo creek to

Terrace creek was no more than ten miles. If he left his pack behind, he could probably pull through. He had never finished a day in the mountains yet without another ten miles up his sleeve.

His back was wet with sweat from carrying the pack, and he shivered with the cold. The cold was nibbling at him, at his nose, at his cheeks, crawling like a wet thing across his back. He forced his hands into his mittens, shoved them through the thongs of his ski poles and started off. He did not need to grasp the poles tightly. His hands rested upon the thongs which bore the weight he put upon them. His fingers did not pain him. He felt no sensations in them at all and his feet might have been pieces of wood strapped within his ski boots.

He crossed the river and angled up the slope towards the ridge that lay between him and the Moose. When he came out of the timber, the moon threw his shadow on the snow, a shadow faltering and stooped as if at any minute it might leave him, send him on alone to go shadowless through the moonlight. His shadow became a burden, something he pulled beside him in the snow.

He climbed high above the timber. The wind blew before him the long ends of the red neckerchief that he wore tied around the collar of his mackinaw, and near him the moon threw the outlines of a peak black upon the snow, black as ink seeping through the snow. Conroy paused a moment, leaned against a snow bank, sank down into it and rested.

How good to rest! How soft and warm the snow! There was the valley below him, empty in the moonlight — the clearing in thc forest, timber that looked small and black as marsh grass. Across from him was a line of peaks thrust up against the sky, notched and jagged as if old bones, half covered with the snow, littered their crests. To his left was the pass, a low saddle in the mountains, where he had crossed in the afternoon.

From below, somewhere in the forest, a wolf howled.

Conroy glanced upwards over his shoulder. He had still six

hundred feet to climb to the ridge above the Moose, above the cabin at Terrace creek where MacMoran waited. MacMoran would take him in, feed him, make a fire for him to sit beside. He gathered his muscles together, summoned his strength that was slipping from him like a loosened garment. Then he lay back for another moment, to rest.

When he opened his eyes again, the moon had gone. The red sun, topping the range across the valley, shone upon him. His neckerchief flapped in the wind on the snow beside his cheek. He had slipped lower, fallen over upon his side, his face turned towards the route he had followed where his half-obliterated ski trail led down to the timber, the stunted spruce and balsam that seemed to be on their way towards him.

He heard horse bells. It was winter and no horses were within a hundred miles. He heard streaming river water. He heard a wide brown river running over mossy boulders between low banks of grass and willow. Across the valley he saw a cottage he had never seen before — a white cottage, low roofed, with green trees beside it and an open door.

Then he remembered that he was on his way to MacMoran's cabin on Terrace creek. MacMoran would be waiting for him. He tried to rise, but his arms stayed at his side. Snow had drifted over them. A weight was on them that he could not lift. They were heavy with the burden of their own inertia. Snow like a blanket covered his body and the wind blew snow against his face.

For a moment he thought again of Macdonald who had brought his frozen feet to the railroad. Macdonald frowned and shook his head, opened his mouth and spoke some words that Conroy could not hear.

They would come and get him, Conroy thought — Macdonald, MacMoran, someone would come and get him. They were camped now down by Hoodoo cabin. They would see his trail and come and get him. He would lie for a while and wait.

Later, the pale cold sun was high in the sky. It shone full

upon him. But the light of the sun was dim, as if a brighter light shone from behind it and the sunlight was its shadow. He could not see across the valley now, where the white cottage with the open door and the green trees had been. The world was growing small, dying slowly in the darkness of the sunlight.

Tunnel Mountain

George Bowering

On the bare top
of Tunnel Mountain
pushed up over
the neat handicraft
of Banff

there is a clean
carving in the rock:

    William Jackson
    June 7 1894

where the Rocky Mountain
wind never stops
blowing over the edge
to the green firs
a mile below.

Wind blew in 1894
wcst to cast,
& people write poems
to Rocky Mountains.

People write names
in mountains
& come down
where the wind blows
around things.

A Trip to Mt. Edith Cavell

H. E. Bulyea

Ever since my first glimpse of Mt. Edith Cavell from a GTP car window during a trip through the mountains in 1918 I had longed for a more intimate acquaintance. The chance came last fall when some Edmonton people had been invited to share the hospitality of the YMCA for a time after the regular camp period had expired. I was fortunate enough to be included in the list, and on Wednesday, the 3rd of September, we were met at Jasper station by the genial Secretary, Mr. Will Green, who escorted us to their well-appointed and beautiful camp on the shore of Lake Edith, four miles east of the town.

The first day in camp was beautifully warm and bright, but the next looked like a change to less agreeable weather, so we did not venture far from camp but joined a party going to Pyramid Lake. While there the expected storm came and we returned to camp, slightly damp but otherwise feeling fine after a very enjoyable outing. The next day it rained again and for several days we did little but sit about the big camp fire and prophesy about the weather or endeavour to cheer up those whose spirits seemed to droop in sympathy with their dampened crinolines. "All things come to those who wait," we told our fair companions and on Sunday we had our predictions verified when once more the peaks across the lake began to show through the mists. The beauty of the scenery had been added to behind the screen of clouds, snow covered all the upper slopes, and the sight was ample reward for all our patient waiting.

Next day I induced a young man, whom we shall call "Mac," to join me on the contemplated expedition to Mount Edith Cavell, and the following early morning saw us on our way, each carrying a blanket, a few sandwiches, a camera and other necessary articles. After a four-mile hike to town we took the trail running up the west side of the Athabaska, where a motor road was being built, and for about nine miles the going was good. The views along the river in many places were charming, Maligne Mountains to the left, Mt. Hardisty far up the river, the Whistlers to the right and our goal, with its mantle of white, much of the time showing straight in front; we had surroundings and incentive sufficient to suit the most fastidious.

About noon we reached the roadbuilders' camp at Astoria Creek where we tucked a good square meal under our belts, which somewhat added to our satisfaction and saved our own scanty hoard for future use. Then we crossed the bridge over the creek and began our ascent of a big hill where a gang of men were cutting out a "switch-back". Near the top we met friend Bruin coming towards us on the trail. The year before the greetings of the furry denizens had been brought by a brown bear, but this time a big black fellow came, who seemed anxious to have the agony of our acquaintance over in a hurry, so without much ceremony he handed over the freedom of the road and on we went.

The aforesaid "switch-back" when finished will be one of the attractions of the trip. It winds back and forth half-a-dozen times in making the crest of the hill (which must be five or six hundred feet in height) by an easy grade and the views on the way will be most magnificent.

Reaching the top we then took a pony trail which follows the edge of a table-land on the east side of the creek. About six miles further we found ourselves at an old camp ground beside a small stream running into the main creek. This we took to be Cavell Creek and we followed it up for some distance before discovering our mistake. After retracing our steps we found the crossing a little farther down, and the well-marked trail led us at length to our goal.

Owing to this miscalculation and other side trips, partly intentional and partly otherwise, we did not reach our destination until nearly dark, but we found an old camp site at the foot of Cavell Lake and here we built a fire, spread our blankets on some fir boughs and turned in for the night.

Mac and I agreed to take turns at keeping the fire going, but evidently each thought the other not to be trusted, so we very frequently, during the first part of the night, went at the task together. Before morning, however, I became convinced that the other fellow was quite capable of performing his duties and I curled up in the blankets and was soon in the land of forgetfulness where I remained until broad daylight. On awakening we discovered to be true what we had suspected during the night, that it had been pretty cold up there near the glacier. The ground was frozen all about us, but our fire had done its duty very well and by frequent turns we had managed to avoid sharing the fate of our surroundings.

Soon the sun was shining on the glacier and we loaded our cameras and went down to the lake. It was a beautiful sight. The bright light on the ice and snow above mirrored in the dark water below were good to look upon, but not so good from the photographer's standpoint. The valley was in deep gloom and the snow-capped peak, a patch of dazzling brightness, made it a proposition for the camera man not easily solved. However, with the aid of ray-filters and numerous experiments in exposure, we managed to get what afterwards passed for fairly good pictures.

Striking as the scene was then it was doubly so at night. The moon shone on the glacier and the awe and stillness, added to the deeper gloom of night in the valley, lent a fascination words cannot describe. I think whoever named that great mass of ice "Ghost Glacier" must have slept there too and watched it in the moonlight.

After breakfast we crossed Cavell Creek and climbed to the tree line for the purpose of getting a view of the beautiful valley to the west. Here, from a rock-slide, I made an exposure. Feeling satisfied with the results of our efforts we descended, but subsequently, greatly to my disappointment, it was found badly out of focus and almost useless.

While photographically our trip was not a great success, in other respects it was eminently so. We had reached our goal under ideal weather conditions and had seen a beautiful country beyond — a country I understand that has been little explored and where the Alpine Club might in the future very profitably and enjoyably hold a camp.

Let me here also mention the fact that my companion, who proved himself a most agreeable and willing partner and who seemed almost not to know fatigue, had been denied the privilege of going to the war on account of a bad heart. Could they have seen him lead up those twenty miles from Jasper to Cavell Lake with almost eight other miles thrown in on the same day I feel sure cardiac murmurs would have been disregarded.

Our return journey was uneventful. Another good meal at the construction camp and the balance of the journey in the moonlight stand out in our memories most, but I would not omit that most delightful sensation of tumbling into a comfortable bed at the end of a tiresome but very pleasant journey.

CROSS-PUR

SES
James P. McLachlan

Jamie

Elizabeth Brewster

When Jamie was sixteen,
Suddenly he was deaf. There were no songs,
No voices any more.
He walked about stunned by the terrible silence.
Kicking a stick, rapping his knuckles on doors,
He felt a spell of silence all about him,
So loud it made a whirring in his ears.
People moved mouths without a sound escaping:
He shuddered at the straining of their throats.
And suddenly he watched them with suspicion,
Wondering if they were talking of his faults,
Were pitying him or seeing him with scorn.
He dived into their eyes and dragged up sneers,
And sauntering the streets, imagined laughter behind him.
Working at odd jobs, ploughing, picking potatoes,
Chopping trees in the lumber woods in winter,
He became accustomed to an aimless and lonely labor.
He was solitary and unloquacious as a stone,
And silence grew over him like moss on an old stump.
But sometimes, going to town,

He was sore with the hunger for company among the people,
And, getting drunk, would shout at them for friendship,
Laughing aloud in the streets.
He returned to the woods,
And dreaming at night of a shining cowboy heaven
Where guns crashed through his deafness, woke morose,
And chopped the necks of pine trees in his anger.

Babe and the Bully

R. Ross Annett

In the Star Store, in Sanford, Joe happened upon a full-length mirror and, with the self-conscious air of a man who never got more than a head-and-shoulders view of himself in the small looking glass at home, he paused to take stock of his appearance.

He thought he looked pretty smart. His blue Sunday suit was kind of tight through the chest and shoulders, but it looked good with the fancy red-and-gold tie which the kids had given him for his birthday. He had shaved before leaving home, and trimmed his black mustache carefully. As soon as he arrived in town he had got a haircut. It had left a band of white skin showing between his black hair and his sun-browned face and neck.

Joe was fussy about his appearance that morning because he was anxious to make a good impression upon the new banker. He had to borrow money to carry him until after harvest. As he resumed his progress toward the store's street entrance, carrying the bag of groceries and his empty egg crate, he frowned at the thought of the distasteful chore ahead of him. He always disliked having to go — hat in hand, so to speak — to ask for a loan, and the fact that the new bank manager was a stranger to him made it more of an ordeal than usual.

On the sidewalk in front of the store, Babe was trying out a new skipping rope which Joe had just bought for her. At the sight of her, Joe's frown vanished. She wore a summery, light-blue dress. Her cheeks were flushed and rosy, and her blue eyes sparkling. As she skipped, her fair hair tossed in the sunshine and her fluffy dress rose and fell rhythmically about her round bare legs. Joe paused in the doorway to watch her. Babe was the picture of her mom. He wished that Emmy could have lived to see her now.

Joe's decrepit old pickup was parked at the curb, and Little Joe was leaning against the side of it, watching Babe with the bored but tolerant air of an older brother. Little Joe took after his pop. He had the same black hair and eyes, and the same sturdy build. He would be a big man someday — and a lot better man, Joe hoped, than his pop was. Refined, sort of, like his mom's folks; not rough and common, like Joe himself or Uncle Pete.

"I want that you kids should be genteel an' refined like your mom was," Joe often told them.

While he lingered, admiring them, a boy came along the sidewalk and stopped to watch Babe skipping. He was taller than Little Joe, but skinny. He wore a fancy, striped T shirt and brand-new jeans and sneakers. The only untidy thing about him was his tousled, sandy hair.

"I can walk on my hands," he announced presently. Without waiting for an invitation, he proceeded to demonstrate while, unobserved in the doorway, Joe grinned indulgently. *You take a boy,* he was thinking. *Seems like he's always gotta show off in front of a girl.* It would not be many years, Joe supposed, before some boy would be trying to impress a teen-aged Babe with a hot-rod car or a half-broke cow pony.

Babe stopped skipping. She and Little Joe looked on admiringly as the boy teetered along on his hands. A pocket-knife and sundry nails, bottle caps and other small objects fell from his pockets one by one and clattered to the sidewalk. Finally, he dropped his feet to the sidewalk and began picking the things up.

"You want to wrastle?" he challenged Little Joe.

"O.K.," Little Joe answered, with a reluctance which his pop could understand, the other boy being so much bigger. But Joe did not interfere. He believed in letting his kids fight their own battles.

The boys approached each other warily. After some preliminary feints, the big boy grabbed Little Joe about the neck. But Little Joe got his arms around his adversary's waist and, by dint of much straining and grunting, wrestled the kid to the sidewalk and held him there, flat on his back and helpless, for all his squirming.

"Nice goin', boy!" Big Joe applauded under his breath.

After a time, Little Joe got to his feet and waited for the other boy to start another round. But the kid did not offer to resume the bout. With a sulky air, he began brushing the dust off his new clothes. Then, in an obvious attempt to recover the prestige he had lost when thrown by a smaller boy, he took a crumpled cigarette from his pocket and a match. He lit the cigarette and nonchalantly tossed the match away. Suddenly, he jerked the skipping rope from Babe's hands and took off on the run.

"Hey! Bring that back!" Little Joe cried, starting in pursuit.

Big Joe dropped the egg crate and the bag of groceries. He shot out of the store like an angry bull coming out of a rodeo chute, passing Little Joe in a few bounds. Where Babe was concerned, it was hard for Joe to hold to the principle of non-interference in kids' squabbles. Because Babe was just a little thing, little and fair and dainty, and so much like her mom.

The kid kept waving the rope tauntingly as he ran. By and by he glanced over his shoulder and noticed that his pursuer was not Little Joe, but a big and angry man who was overtaking him rapidly. With a sharp "Yipe!" of panic, he dropped the rope and tossed away his cigarette. Then he rocketed ahead so fast that, instead of overtaking him, Joe began to drop farther behind.

A maroon-and-cream sedan was parked in front of the butcher's. The kid raced up to the car, yanked open a door and dived inside, pulling the door shut after him. When Joe charged up a moment later, the boy was cowering against a stout, ruddy-faced man behind the wheel.

"Is this young bully your boy, mister?" Joe demanded.

"He is," said the stout man, bristling. Joe did not know the man. He was wearing a gray business suit and a pearl-gray hat.

"You oughta learn him to pick on kids his own size," Joe said.

"Try picking on people your own size yourself," sneered the stout man.

In view of the stranger's uncooperative attitude, there was not much that Joe could do. The man was a soft and flabby type. It would not be right for Joe to work him over. Joe turned his smoldering eyes on the boy.

"In future, you young bully," he said, "leave my little girl alone."

Then he turned away. He retrieved the skipping rope and strode back to the pickup where Babe and Little Joe were waiting. He handed Babe the skipping rope and carried the groceries and the egg crate out from the store.

"He's not a very nice boy," Babe said. "He smoked, pop!"

"I seen him, Baby," Big Joe said. He frowned, observing a look of reluctant admiration for the bully in Babe's wide blue eyes and Little Joe's black ones.

"The boy swore, too, pop!" Babe said solemnly. But there was still that look in her eyes, as though, for all her virtuous tone of voice, she could not help regarding the kid as a hero. "People shouldn't swear," she said.

"Damn tooting' they shouldn't!" Big Joe said.

"You swore, pop!" Babe chided.

"Dad rat it!" he exploded irritably. He always tried to set a proper example for Babe and Little Joe, but sometimes a swear word slipped out. It made him feel ashamed.

"I ain't very refined," he admitted gruffly. Then, to change the subject, he demanded, "Who was that kid, anyway?"

"His name is Eddie," Little Joe answered. "Eddie Walton."

"His father works in the bank," Babe said.

"Oh, no!" ejaculated Big Joe.

The kids looked up at him anxiously.

"What's the matter, pop?" they asked in unison.

Without waiting to reply, Joe whirled about and started back along the street, almost running. If he hoped to get a bank loan, he would have to apologize to the banker. Otherwise the guy would take great delight in brushing off a man who had called his son a bully.

"I guess I was kind of hasty," Joe would say. "You know how it is, mister: A man flies off the handle sometimes. After all" — Joe practised a tolerant chuckle — "kids will be kids, like the fellow says. I guess your boy was only foolin'."

He even persuaded himself that the boy was not really a bully, but had merely been trying to show off, the way boys are prone to do.

However, all Joe's feverish rehearsing was wasted. The maroon-and-cream sedan had gone. It was nowhere in sight.

"Brother!" Joe mourned. "I sure won't get no loan from that guy now!"

But with all the harvest expenses looming up — gas and oil and machinery repairs and what not — he had to raise some money somewhere. Or else he would have to sell a few steers, even though not a critter on the place was ready for market.

As he pondered glumly upon his predicament, the only way out that he could think of was to get the kids' Uncle Pete to apply to the bank for a loan. Joe was far from hopeful about this idea, because Pete had no standing with banks and bankers. In fact, Pete had no standing, period. Respectable people looked askance at him because he was a heavy drinker and, worse still, made his own liquor so as to assure himself a constant supply. The police were always laying for him, not only because of his still but because occasionally, when he needed money, he would sell a gallon or two of moonshine to Tom Dunke, the Sanford bootlegger. Pete was not notably scrupulous, either, about paying his debts. Nobody who knew him would lend him a dollar. But — and this was the one thing Joe counted on — the new banker did not know Pete, and might therefore take his signature on a note. There would be no risk to the bank in this, because Joe would see that the note was paid when it came due.

You generally knew where to find Pete when he was in town. Joe stopped at the drugstore and bought a small bag of peppermints, then walked on a couple of blocks and turned into the bar of the Farmers' and Ranchers' Hotel. He himself never went into the place except when he was looking for Pete. Joe did not drink. He had promised Emmy.

"Don't get to be an old soak like Pete. For the children's sake," Emmy used to say.

Sure enough, Pete was in the bar. He and Tom Dunke had their heads together.

"I gotta talk to you, Pete," Joe said, giving Dunke only a curt nod.

Pete followed Joe out to the street, walking with the slouching, bowlegged gait of the veteran cowpoke. He was a head shorter than Joe, and kind of scrawny. But he was a tough old rascal. Otherwise he could never have stood the life he had led and the liquor he had drunk.

Liquor had marked him, though. His eyes were red-rimmed and watery; his nose and cheeks mottled with a net-work of purplish veins. He had a dumb and sodden look that often deceived strangers. Because Pete was not nearly so dumb as he appeared.

"I want you to go to the bank an' see can you borrow four hundred bucks," Joe said.

"Who? Me?" asked Pete incredulously. He suffered from chronic asthma, which made his voice harsh and rasping, like the sound of a rusty hinge. Pete knew that nobody but a Santa Claus would take a chance on lending him money. And Santa Clauses did not get to bank managers.

"I just had some words with the new banker," Joe explained. He told Pete about the trouble over Babe's skipping rope. "I didn't know he was the new banker, see? I called his kid a bully an' he got sore. Chances are, he wouldn't loan me a nickel now. But he might maybe let you have the money. It's worth a try, anyway."

He grew more and more pessimistic, however, as he pictured the poor impression Pete would make on a stranger. Pete was never fussy about his appearance. His old ten-gallon hat was soiled and tattered. His shirt and pants were shabby, the pants tucked into badly scuffed cowboy boots that were grotesquely run over at the heels. In fact, Pete looked like a tramp. Even his breath was against him, although Joe had bought the peppermints to take care of that.

"Take a mouthful of these before you go in the bank," he warned, thrusting the bag into Pete's hand.

Pete put a handful of peppermints in his mouth at once and began chomping on them. But he looked mighty dubious as he turned away. After a dozen shuffling steps, he halted.

"Did you tell this banker your name?" he asked over his shoulder.

"I didn't have no chance," Joe answered.

"I got a idee, then," Pete said thoughtfully. One rheumy eyelid drooped in a sly wink. "Don't worry about a thing, Joe," he said. He put some more peppermints in his mouth and started for the bank.

Joe looked after him uneasily. The kind of "idees" that came to Pete often led to highly improper and illegal acts. Still and all, Joe did not see how Pete could break any law by merely asking for a loan. The worst that could — and very probably would — happen was that the banker would refuse him. Joe returned to the pickup and sat waiting in the cab.

Babe, meanwhile, had resumed her skipping. She skipped all the way down the block, with Little Joe sauntering aimlessly beside her. They had stopped to admire a new car in the window of the Sanford Garage when a voice behind them said, "Hi, kids!"

They turned their heads, and Babe clutched her skipping rope more tightly when she saw the Walton boy behind them. However, he seemed to be in a meek and chastened mood.

"Your dad scared hell outta me," he said.

"You shouldn't swear," Babe said primly. But she gave him a faint smile which took the sting out of her reproof.

"I was only teasin' you about the skippin' rope," Eddie Walton said. "I was goin' to bring it back." As if anxious to make amends, he asked, "Would you kids like some ice cream?"

"O.K.," Little Joe answered.

Eddie began searching through his pockets. "I guess I gotta get some money from my dad first," he said finally. "You kids come with me."

They walked together towards the bank. Little Joe thought it must be nice to have a father who worked in a bank where all the money was. He said as much to Eddie, and Eddie answered, "Oh, sure!"

Even if he did smoke and swear, or perhaps because of his daring to do so, and also because his father worked in a bank where all the money was, Babe and Little Joe felt drawn to him. Babe began to skip again as they moved along. Then she let Eddie try it, but he could not skip very well. His feet became tangled in the rope and they all got to laughing. At the door of the bank, however, Babe and Little Joe hung back shyly.

"Come on!" Eddie urged. He grabbed their hands and practically dragged them inside.

The manager's office was just inside the front door, an arrangement which had seemed providential to Uncle Pete. He had been able to sneak in without being seen by the rest of the bank staff, some of whom, he feared, might know him by sight. When Pete entered, the manager was sitting at a big mahogany desk. He was a stout man with gray eyes that looked up at Pete frostily. Seemed like, to Pete, that bankers' eyes always had a frosty look. He guessed it was one of the qualifications a man had to have to become a banker.

"Howdy!" Pete said. As he said it, unfortunately, one of the unconsumed peppermints shot out of his mouth and slithered across the typed letter which the manager was in the act of signing. The banker looked at the smeared letter and then, with an expression of annoyance, he crumpled up the letter and threw it, peppermint and all, into the wastepaper basket.

Somewhat dismayed at this inauspicious beginning, Pete nevertheless cleared his throat and inquired, "Could I git to borry four hundred dollars?"

Mr. Walton looked at him sourly. Undoubtedly he had sized Pete up as one of the local dead beats who made a practice of calling on a new bank manager, hoping to put the bite on him for a loan before he had a chance to learn about their reputations. But Pete had already decided that it was hopeless to ask for a loan in his own name. Joe, however, had a good credit rating at the bank, although he dared not appear in person at the moment to make use of it. As Pete saw it, therefore, all he had to do was to give Joe's name instead of his own. He did so, adding that he had often got loans from the bank in the past and had repaid them when due.

At this, the banker's face registered surprise and disbelief. He pulled out a drawer in a filing cabinet and pawed through it, eventually lifting out a large form. Pete knew what it was: the statement of assets which Joe had given the former manager the last time he had applied for a loan. Bankers, like cops, were always great ones for keeping a man's record. In Pete's case, of course, it was the cops who kept the record. As Mr. Walton scanned Joe's statement his gray eyes lost a little of their former frostiness.

"Sit down, Joe," he said. "Let's bring this statement of yours up to date."

Quite at his ease now, Pete sat down in the customer's chair beside the desk. He answered the banker's questions as promptly as Joe himself could have done. Because Pete knew all the answers: the section numbers of Joe's deeded land; how many sections of grazing lease Joe held; the number of cattle sold off during the year, and the present size of his herd.

After that, there was nothing to it. The banker filled out a note form and passed it across to Pete for his signature. Pete had a deep-seated distrust of all banks and bankers which warned him not to sign even Joe's name to a paper that he had not read carefully. He held the note at arm's length, therefore, and squinted at the fine print on it, explaining with wry humor as he did so, "I can still see good, only nowadays, seems like, my arm ain't hardly long enough."

Satisfied at last, he took the pen and signed Joe's name to the note, imitating Joe's signature as nearly as he could. He realized that, technically, he was committing a forgery and that bankers took a dim view of forgery. But he excused himself on the ground that the money was being borrowed for Joe on Joe's own credit and that Joe would repay it when due. Moreover, Mr. Walton did not know Pete from Adam's off ox, and if he kept out of the banker's sight — as he had a fervent intention of doing — until after the note was due, there was little chance of the forgery being discovered. At his request, the bank manager got the cash from the teller, thus making it unnecessary for Pete to show himself in the outer office. Then, with a mumbled "Thanks, mister," Pete made a stealthy exit.

Being a man of few scruples, Pete could not fail to recognize a golden opportunity for profit if only Joe would consider exploiting it to the full. If Joe would refuse payment when the note came due, on the ground that his signature had been forged, then the four hundred dollars need never be paid back and the banker would be left holding the bag. And there was nobody in the world that Pete would rather swindle out of four hundred dollars than a banker. But he had to put the enticing idea regretfully aside. He knew better than to suggest such a scheme to Joe, who was always scrupulously honest. Indeed, Pete thought it wise not to let on how he had tricked the banker. Joe would probably be crazy enough to take the money right back. Then the banker would sick the police on Pete, and Joe would still not get a loan, the banker being sore at him.

Joe was waiting in the pickup in front of the Star Store. He was surprised and greatly relieved when Pete handed over the roll of bills.

"There wasn't nothin' to it," Pete said. "Now let's round up the kids an' git outta town — before," he added under his breath, "we run into that banker an' he finds out which one of us is Joe." He hopped into the cab and they cruised slowly along the main street.

"Well, what d'ye know!" Joe growled presently. He had caught sight of the banker emerging from Slade's Confectionery. Babe and Little Joe and the Walton boy were with him. All three kids had ice-cream sticks. Babe was holding Mr. Walton's hand and talking a blue streak while the banker smiled down at her. Babe was always a happy little tyke, the sort of kid that most grownups smiled at. "Looks like they've made friends," Joe said. "Maybe, I put you to a lot of trouble for nothin', Pete."

But it seemed to Pete that his troubles might be just starting. He dropped to his hands and knees in the narrow space between the seat and the dash.

"What the heck are you doin', Pete?" Joe demanded in astonishment.

"I ain't doin' push-ups," Pete answered in a surly voice.

"Are you sick or somethin'?"

"Dizzy, sort of," Pete said. "Git me to a doctor, quick! Don't stop to talk to nobody!"

Joe had started to pull up, but now he stepped on the gas, intending to dash past the group on the sidewalk without stopping. But Babe let go the banker's hand and darted out on the street, waving the ice-cream stick in one hand and the skipping rope in the other.

"Oo-hoo! Pop!" she called.

So Joe was forced to stop, in spite of Pete's profane protests.

"Mr. Walton bought us some ice cream!" Babe cried, running up. "This is Mr. Walton, pop."

By this time Pete was fairly hugging the floorboards.

He must be real sick, Joe worried. *Cramps, maybe.* But Joe had to pause long enough to give the banker a polite "Howdy." You had to be polite to a banker.

"Pleased to meet you, Mr. Walton," he said. "I guess I was kind of hasty there a while back. I guess your boy was only teasin', sort of."

"Sure!" Little Joe put in. "Eddie's a nice guy, pop."

The banker smiled. He seemed now to be a friendly man. And even if he had not been a banker, Joe would have been favorably disposed to any man who took kindly to Joe's kids.

"They've ironed out their differences, apparently," Mr. Walton chuckled. "You've got a fine son and a very charming little daughter, Mr. —ah—I still don't know your name."

At the latter statement, Pete took new heart. He thought he might still escape detection if he could get Joe away at once. But if Joe once gave his name, the banker would say: "That's queer, I just lent some money to a man by that name." And then the fat would really be in the fire.

"Let's git the hell outta here!" Pete urged in a harsh undertone that reminded Joe of Pete's need for a doctor.

"I gotta git along," Joe said hastily.

He was letting in the clutch when Little Joe caught sight of the humped-up seat of Pete's pants.

"What's Uncle Pete doin'?" the boy cried curiously. Worse still he pulled the cab door open — and instantly recoiled at the sight of Pete's scowling face. The scowl changed to a furtive and guilty look as Pete climbed back on the seat under the banker's puzzled glance.

"This is Mr. Walton, Uncle Pete," Babe said brightly.

"Pete ain't feeling well," Big Joe said.

"Pete?" echoed the banker.

"Nickname," Pete said thickly, still trying. "Lots of folks call me Pete."

"He acts like he's gone off his rocker," Joe said. "I gotta get him to a Doctor."

"Just a minute," the banker objected. "He told me his name was Joe."

"That's what I mean about him bein' off his head. Because I'm Joe. He's my brother, Pete."

"Never mind about a doctor then. What we need is a policeman," the banker said sharply. He did not look a bit friendly now. The frosty look was back in his eye, and his voice had the chill of a forty below zero day. "Did you know that this man signed your name to a note?" the banker demanded of Joe.

"Good grief, no!" Joe gasped . . . "That's forgery, Pete! They put you in jail for forgery!"

Pete did not say anything. He just gave Joe a bitter look.

"I s'pose he thought he was helpin' me out." Joe said. He blamed himself, really. He should have known better than to trust Pete, especially in a bank. "I was goin' to ask you for a loan, Mr. Walton," Joe said, "but we had words about your boy. So I figured you wouldn't gimme a loan after that."

"I don't let personalities influence me in matters of business," Mr. Walton said huffily. "If you rated a loan — and, on your record, you do — I'd have given it to you."

"I didn't know," Joe said ruefully. "So I sent Pete to the

bank to see could he borrow the money. I thought that was the way he got it.''

He took the roll of bills from his pocket and handed it to the banker. Seemed like everything had gone sour. And not only about the money. Unless Joe talked fast and persuasively to the banker, Pete would likely be sent to jail for forgery. As always, Joe worried most about the impact of this upon Babe and Little Joe. They would be shamed before all their kid friends if their uncle was put in jail.

So far, Babe and Little Joe had been joshing with the Walton boy, not paying much attention to their elders. Mr. Walton took a half dollar from his pocket.

''Eddie,'' he said, ''go buy Babe and Little Joe some more ice cream.''

He looked after them as they trooped joyfully away.

''You failed to declare all your assets on your bank statement, Joe,'' he said.

''Oh-oh!'' Joe muttered. Apparently both he and Pete were in trouble. He noticed, however, that there was a twinkle in the banker's eye.

''In my opinion,'' Mr. Walton said, ''Babe and Little Joe are your chief assets.''

''Damn tootin'!'' Joe agreed heartily. To him, it was not by any means a novel idea. Indeed, with her bright gold hair, Babe often seemed to him one of the gilt-edged assets that people always talked about. But he was surprised that a banker should be so human-like as to voice such a thought.

''Just to make things regular, Joe,'' Mr. Walton said, ''you'd better come back to the bank with me now and sign a new note.''

''But how about Pete?'' Joe asked. ''He shouldn't ought've done it, but he was only trying' to get me out of a spot.''

''I'm going to let Pete off with a warning.'' the banker said, looking at Pete severely. . . . ''Don't you ever try anything criminal again, Pete,'' he said.

''Hnh-uh'' Pete answered, emphatically. But, of course, he

was just saying that. Joe had not much hope of Pete ever learning to be honest and respectable. In fact, if Babe and Little Joe were assets, like the banker said, Pete was certainly the family's greatest liability.

Later, while they were driving homeward in the pickup, Babe said dreamily, "It must be nice to work in a bank."

"Where all the money is," Little Joe added.

Uncle Pete chuckled hoarsely. "I'd sure like to work in a bank — some night," he said.

The Alberta Homesteader

Anonymous

My name is Dan Gold, an old bach'lor I am,
I'm keeping old batch on an elegant plan.
You'll find me out here on Alberta's bush plain
A-starving to death on a government claim.

So come to Alberta, there's room for you all
Where the wind never ceases and the rain always falls,
Where the sun always sets and there it remains
Till we get frozen out on our government claims.

My house it is built of the natural soil,
My walls are erected according to Hoyle,
My roof has no pitch, it is level and plain,
And I always get wet when it happens to rain.

My clothes are all ragged, my language is rough,
My bread is case-hardened and solid and tough,
My dishes are scattered all over the room,
My floor gets afraid at the sight of a broom.

How happy I feel when I roll into bed,
The rattlesnake rattles a tune at my head.
The little mosquito devoid of all fear
Crawls over my face and into my ear.

The little bed-bug so cheerful and bright,
It keeps me up laughing two thirds of the night,
And the smart little flea with tacks in his toes
Crawls up through my whiskers and tickles my nose.

You may try to raise wheat, you may try to raise rye,
You may stay there and live, you may stay there and die,
But as for myself, I'll no longer remain
A-starving to death on a government claim.

So farewell to Alberta, farewell to the west,
It's backwards I'll go to the girl I love best.
I'll go back to the east and get me a wife
And never eat cornbread the rest of my life.

An Old-Timer Remembers

''Seventy''

We came to Alberta in 1911. The children and I arrived in Calgary in June, on the coronation day of King George V and Queen Mary. The whole place was crowded, and we could not get a room anywhere: so we went back to the train and came on north.

On that train-trip I saw my first Mountie and his prisoner, whom he was taking to Fort Saskatchewan jail. A Roman Catholic priest was with them, and eventually they all got off the train together.

I wasn't long on the farm until I tried duck-hunting for the first time. Wild ducks kept quacking on a slough surrounded by high grain a little north of us. So I borrowed a shotgun, though I had never used one before, and sneaked through the grain until I was at the slough's edge. Then I stood up, scaring the ducks into flight. At once I let drive into the middle of them and actually got two. Nobody was as surprised as I was!

During my forty-three years in Alberta I've helped dig wells and cellars; I've helped build and shingle buildings, and paint them inside and out. I've cut, raked and bucked prairie and slough hay (there's a difference) and helped with the stacking. I've driven the binder; and stooked; and bound sheaves with their own stems, so they stayed "put". I've broken horses, to lead and ride and work, and had cows to milk. I've hand-fed calves and lambs and a colt and raised quite a lot of motherless chickens and turkeys. I've sheared sheep and washed and carded the wool and quilted about forty quilts — light in weight, and very warm. I've made my own soap (it's very good and lasts well) and I've used a horse to snake in poplar and willow poles, up to six inches in diameter, for wood. I've picked roots on new breaking and piled and burned them. It's rather fun seeing a new field in the making: you usually pick the roots two or three times, while it's being disked and harrowed.

All Alberta women like me have cut lots of wood with a cross-cut saw, a buck-saw or axe, and cut up roots, too — a hard task, but they yield good, long-lasting firewood. We've picked blueberries by the pailful, using the home-made jam-tin pickers with nails on one side and a handle opposite. You clean the berries by letting the wind blow out the trash and leaves. We used to get lots of wild gooseberries as well, twenty or thirty quarts a year. I would often read while stemming them, and get rested up at the same time.

I've helped put out prairie fires with a wet gunny-sack dipped occasionally in a pail of water carried along, or in some ditch or slough on my way. (I saw a real prairie fire on Christmas Day — about 1914 or '15, I think. There was no snow, just a patch here and there.)

My first Alberta baby was a neighbour's. One dark night I waited in her three-room shack until the doctor came out of the bedroom with the very new baby wrapped in a blanket and put it into my arms, saying "Here's your baby." I felt sort of lost at first, since the doctor and nurse left at once — but from her bed the mother started telling me what to do and how to do it. Since this was her fifth or sixth, the baby was soon slicked up and comfy, and the mother resting nicely.

Alberta farm folk get used to little wild creatures around them. Every summer I saw lots of wee prairie chicken and partridge chicks in their pretty striped suits. Stumble across a flock and, in the twinkling of an eye, not onc is in sight! So you start feeling around, very carefully, in each tuft of grass; and finally you get one. How he would peep and jump, his little heart beating madly! After you'd petted him to the stage where he closed his eyes, you'd put him down in the grass. Instantly he'd straighten up, get his bearings, then dart away under some leaves or more grass. All this time, the mother would be frantically clucking and scolding and limping around, first with one wing "broken", and then the other . . . trying so hard to get your attention. Such little dramas broke the loneliness and, somehow renewed, you'd go back to your berry-picking.

One day, an elderly woman and I started out to visit some neighbours two or three miles away. We came to a medium-sized slough that looked fairly dry on the outer edge, though there was quite a stretch of water in the middle. We decided to try crossing, but the moment we got out to the stagnant water the horse began to sink. The farther we went, the deeper the horse sank, until he was over his knees in very sticky mud. Then he got scared and began to plunge. Finally, about half way across, he stopped struggling. I was afraid he would lie down — and a "down" horse can drown in a very few inches of water. I took off my shoes and stockings, tucked up my skirts, and stepped out into that ooze. I talked to the horse quietly while I unhitched him. My friend stayed in the buggy. I took the halter rope and went well out in front of the horse and began coaxing him to try again. Soon I had him on better ground — covered with mud, scared and trembling. I wondered if I could leave my friend high and dry in the floating buggy while I went for help, but she flatly refused. Off went her shoes and stockings, and down she came into that sticky mud and water. Unfortunately she slipped, with the result that her lovely white underthings were white no longer. Undaunted, up she got, and together we pushed the rig to shore. We had a very nice visit and a cup of tea . . . and we took the long road home.

I've done quite a lot of fancy-work, taken care of range cattle, made a hobby of photography, collected stamps — I've got about two thousand — and I've done all the ordinary house and farm work and raised my children at the same time.

You may say no one person could have done all this. Well, I have — and most of us Old-Timers can say the same. Today I'm over seventy. I would not have missed it for anything.

Lizards, Lizards, Lizards

Robert Martin

Robert Martin (1858-1942) was one of hundreds of young men from Ontario who came out west to file on a homestead in the year when the Canadian Pacific Railway line was being built across what was later to be the Province of Saskatchewan. In 1883 he made his home in Regina, went into business, and practised his profession of pharmacy; for the rest of his life he was a leader in the business, professional, civic, and educational life of his city and province. He served as mayor of Regina, as a member of the Senate of the University of Saskatchewan, and as president of the Canadian Pharmaceutical Association. The following passages are taken directly from his Diary as published in Saskatchewan History *(1953).*

Broadview to Regina, 1882

Sunday, Aug. 20, 1882

Awoke this a.m. at 6:30. No more sleep for us. Bruce got up

and I next. Got out and gazed on the scene around Broadview. This is the terminus (so far) of the CPR, therefore there are numbers of cars and engines in the yard. Our tent is pitched on the south side of and about 100 yards from the track. West of us is the city, built on both sides of the track. All tents with few exceptions. There are 17 stores, eating houses (called high-toned names), a few shops, blacksmith, etc. To the south of us a few miles distant is a ridge of high land called the "Scrub Hills". Nearer us to the south is a party of surveyors' camps — carts, waggons, etc. North across the track are the tents belonging to the Police and a few Indian camps. The prairie is almost flat, slightly rolling, very little wood, good water. It was not long until we were all up. Alex and Bruce take the oxen about half a mile away to good pasture and tie them to stakes. Martin and I take a pail each and towels and soap and cross the R.R. for water. I take a good wash in a slough, head and feet. Returning, find a big old Indian visiting our camp. He was wrapped in a big Buffalo skin, had yellow beads in his hair, couldn't speak a word of English. He sat down near the stove watching our pot boil. Soon after eight or nine squaws in paint and beads, with youngsters came round and picked up the heads of some ducks (Alex and Martin shot yesterday). Soon after, about 100 young fellows from the neighbouring tents (railroaders) paid us a visit. We chatted with some, and soon we were alone again. We had porridge for Breakfast made from "x lut" which we got in Brandon. After breakfast we were again visited by Indians. The bucks wear a kind of leggings which come up to their thighs, and a shirt (often red flannel) which comes down and meets their nether garments. These today were decorated with beads strung on their long hair. The squaws, some rather nice looking, painted with pink striped with blue. The old fellow filled his pipe, and the young chap lit it for him. He tried to explain to me why the squaws were taking the ducks heads . . .

Monday, August 21st.

We are up at 5:30 busy getting ready for our start across the prairie. We intend shipping our whole truck to the end of the CPR or, at least, as far as we could — but the contractors wouldn't under any consideration carry any freight on their trains, so we have to drive. As we had to add other stuff to our outfit, we were delayed with that and other minor things until 8:15 o'clock. We left Broadview with "Buck and Bright" drawing the well-filled waggon and us fellows all walking. There can be little said of the country over which we passed, just rolling prairie with a very few settlers. We trod along at a three-mile rate until 11:30 when we stopped for dinner. I was cook. We had fried bacon, tea and syrup. We have all good appetites and all satisfied ourselves. Here we organized ourselves. Jack Bruce and I to cook and clean game, Alex and Jack Glanville to wash dishes and pick game, Martin and Bill Castile to attend the oxen, pitch the tent and pack the waggon. About 2:15 we started out again. All the way along we passed several sloughs. The boys managed to bag four wild ducks for our supper. Bruce and Castile pull off their pants to wade for the ducks. Bruce left his off and trudged along the road (trail) two or three miles with his bare legs. About 11 o'clock we crossed Weed Creek — a pretty little stream. About 4 we passed through a nice looking country. Two tents close together. We interviewed both. All Ontario fellows. Passing these we come to a tent where it was said we could get milk. Alex asked a young woman, but we couldn't get any. At 7 we stopped at Summerberry Creek. We were told we'd get plenty of good water here, but alas! there were a few stagnant pools floating with green. There was also a soakage well, but it had just been emptied so we had to use the water out of the pools. We had stewed duck for supper. It was good. The mosquitoes were awful bad. Before bedtime Bill set off a bluff or two of powder. Then about 10 o'clock we went to bed. 18 miles from Broadview. We all felt well and happy.

Wednesday, August 23rd

We rose this a.m. feeling pretty stiff and tired. The mosquitoes were so troublesome that we didn't have a satisfactory sleep. We rose at 4, and after the usual order of packing up, breakfast, and loading everything on the waggon, we started away at 6 o'clock. All forenoon we passed through a pretty picce of country. The sloughs are mostly all dry. A great number of bluffs — small scrubby bushes grow around them. Along the road we raised a covey of prairie chickens. The guns were ahead; however Jack Bruce killed a couple with his revolver. We passed a very pretty spot, quite a lot of timber (poplars) growing on the face of the Squirrel Hills. A pretty field of oats too. At 11:30 we stopped on the Bell Farm, on the bank of a creek for dinner. We had prairie chicken stew. We started again at 1:30. Here we crossed the R.R. track and left the H.B. Co's trail and took the R.R. trail. The H.B. trail turns and goes to N. Qu'Appelle. It is a good road, but the R.R. Trail to S. Qu'Appelle is quite rough. We reached Qu'Appelle at 4 o'clock. A bloomin' town. The far famed Qu'Appelle has 15 tents big and little all told. Not one wooden house. We got six measly loaves of bread for $1.25. They were small but good weight at 4 lbs. each. For miles past this we camped (6:30) for the night. We got good water here. Mosquitoes bad. Had duck for supper. Smoked out the tent after our work was done. South of this is the prettiest country we saw anywhere so far. A great many small bluffs. We fixed the mosquitoes o.k. and went to bed at 9 o'clock.

Thursday, August 24th

We are up at 4:30 feeling tip-top. The night was cool, the mosquitoes vetoed and we had a good sleep. Started at 6. Passed through a really bushy country. Lots of wild ducks; we got several. At 10:30 we stopped for dinner. The day is very hot, hottest we had yet so the oxen played out. While we were eating dinner a man came along on horseback. He stopped and asked us some questions, and told us that he had been up with A. T. Galt to pacify the Indians. We asked him to take some dinner which he did. We had considerable fun asking him questions, etc. He was a queer old codger. While with us he counted his money. He had attempted to take a near cut through a slough, his horse had fallen, and gave him a greal deal of trouble, besides a good soaking. He left us and we got away again at 2. Bill is driving the oxen today. One of his odd expressions is "Move on my firey untamed steeds." They moved on very slowly. At 3:30 we had to stop again and rest the oxen. We stopped for an hour, had a drink with brandy in it. Had more shooting, and stopped at 7 o'clock beside a big slough at 8th siding. Rain, thunder and lightning makes us hurry up pitching tent, getting supper. Don't have a duck for supper. Jack G. is not very well. The mosquitoes are in thousands. We treat them to their usual dose. While we were eating supper the rain came on. We made everything secure and about 9:30 Alex and G. spread their beds. Martin and Jack Bruce were spreading theirs when they noticed a real lizzard on the blanket. To describe the "reptile" — he was about 6 inches long and as big around as my big finger and of a dark mottled green colour — clammy and cold. Can run like sixty; eyes as sharp as a trap. Well it was this chap that the boys discovered on their blanket. We killed and dragged him out of doors. All of us went to bed excepting Bill who was sitting reading. We were just asleep. Everything was quiet when Alex gave a desperate jump and exclaimed: "There's another of those darned lizzards," and so it was, a darned measly lizzard — and had been crawling up Alex's leg — he was killed. I lay for a minute or two and watched the others putting on their clothes. I concluded to do likewise and got up and right where my head was, was another lizzard. Bill got out his big knife and inside of 15 minutes killed seven. Golly our blood ran cold. We all said we'd not go to bed, however after putting on all our clothes, our pants under our sox, our belts tight, a h'kf tied round our heads, a mosquitoe net over our heads, we rolled ourselves in our blankets and went to sleep leaving the lantern burning. Sometime later I awoke and shook a lizzard off my hand. We had a terror of a time.

Saturday, August 26th

The day is pleasant, inclined to be warm. We are 40 miles from Moose Jaw, 6 miles from Pile of Bones Creek. Leaving Boggy Creek at 1:45 we passed over a lovely piece of prairie. Started up a covey of prairie chickens. Shot three which we'll have for Sunday's dinner. We interviewed an Irishman who had just settled on the prairie in June. Came out three or four days after the murder of Cavendish. He told us we could get plenty of fine land within 10 miles of Pile of Bones City (Regina). The land is simply grand. At 8 o'clock we crossed Pile of Bones Creek. Approaching the creek — in the "gloamin" — from the trail the bank runs out like a cape, and one imagines that you could walk about 300 yards and stand on the point but on closer observation shows that there is a horseshoe-shaped hill and a pretty flat valley extending away out for fully half a mile, making a very enchanting scene, perfectly lovely. The creek winds around the horseshoe and the hill is lined with bushes. All around the creek is quite hilly and bushy poplars seven or eight inches thick. The creek is a pretty rippling stream.

Monday, August 28th

We are up at 5 o'clock, feeling well slept. Our Indian scare was a false alarm. At 7:45 we started north — down Pile of Bones Creek — with the intention of going to Long Lake. We kept along the high bank for about a mile or so and came to a deep gully (folks here call them coolies) the oxen had to go round, we descended to a small spring creek at the bottom, fully 200 feet below the top of the bank. Here we found wild grapes, black currants, and raspberries. The currants are as large and some larger than the tame ones. They taste much nicer than the tame ones, more like gooseberries. We got them in abundance and enjoyed them very much. The face of the high banks — (and in fact the whole prairie) — are perfectly covered with rose bushes. Reaching the top again we went a short way and came to another coolie, and here we saw — what I never saw before — a great big fine looking deer, crowned with a handsome pair of horns. He scampered up the hill opposite us and away from us forever. We tried to interview him but he declined having anything to do with us. Next we got to Cotton Wood Creek. Jack and I got separated from all the others and for a short time lost sight of them. We were wandering westward thinking that the waggon had gone that way. After racing up and down hills we looked back and there we saw the remainder of the party climbing the opposite hill — easily 2 miles away from us to the East. To return to them we descended into the valley 200 feet below. Here we climbed over brush, through rose bushes higher than our heads, vines of morning glories, black currants and wild cherries in abundance, across the creek — which is almost dry — and up the opposite hill to where the others were waiting for us. We put in a goodly supply of fruit on the way too, as may readily be supposed. At the top of the hill a discussion takes place. If we want to make use of the R.R. we must not settle on the west side of the Creek, etc., etc. Finally it is concluded to abandon the Lake for today, and instead, to stop a mile or so further up P. of B. Creek, and, while Jack and I bake, the others explore the surrounding country. It is done and at 12 we stop on the bank of the creek in Sec. 13, Tp. 19, Range 22. From here the four started after dinner, two to Big Arm (Qu-Appelle) River (2 miles) and two to go up the Creek to the same River, there to meet and all come home together. While they were away we baked in our oven of sods, cleared things up generally and then tried to fish. We didn't get a bite, because there are no fish to bite. But yet we had the pleasure of seeing the creek, a pretty one to be sure, thickly wooded. From the tent we can see as pretty a valley as imagination can picture, perfectly grand. About 7 the 4 got back and we had supper. Concluded to go on to the Lake tomorrow a.m. The day has been pleasant; tonight is cool. A pretty night (full moon). Go to bed at 10. The land over which we came today to where our camp is, is rich heavy soil, a clay loam.

The Men in Sheepskin Coats

Bruce Hutchison

The postmaster of Gimli, Manitoba, is named Tudni Thorsteinsen. He is an old man now, with curly grey hair, a face which may be properly called beautiful, and fine, clear eyes.

He has held his official position for fifty years, since he came to Canada from Iceland. His daughter does most of the work at the post office now, and this gives him time to complete his memoirs. He writes them on a typewriter in the Icelandic language and then translates them into English. When you sit in his little house, across the village street from the new brick post office, and listen to him read the records of Gimli, you can still see in his old eyes some of the immigrant's lust for land, for settlement, for building. In this neat and shiny sitting room you can see, as well as anywhere, how the blood of foreign races has been poured into the earth of Canada, and guess that in time it will grow a new race here, indigenous to this country, against all calculations and against all race prejudice.

At Gimli everybody is Icelandic. The old folks speak only the language brought with them from home. At the refuge for the aged down the street only one inmate can speak good English. But the younger folk understand both tongues, and many of them have succeeded in the business, professions, and politics of Winnipeg. Two of them have gone to Oxford as Rhodes Scholars, one into the Canadian government.

Mr. Thorsteinsen is proud of his people and sets down their

record faithfully on his little typewriter. Meticulously, as if every date and fact were terribly important, he told me — and waited for me to note everything down at length — how the Icelanders came to Gimli and settled here by Lake Winnipeg because they could fish, as they had fished at home. Through the window now I could see the fish nets hanging on the picket fences and the poplar trees of the garden. By boat in summer and by dogsled on the winter ice the Icelanders go out on the inland sea for their fish harvest, as they used to go into the Atlantic.

Slowly, waiting politely for me to write it down, the postmaster of Gimli read from the record — the first trek from Winnipeg by flat-bottom boats on the river, the original settlement in the cabins of poplar logs and sod roofs, long before his time, the poor crops of wheat and potatoes between the stumps, the starvation, the epidemic, the desertion, the trek to better lands in the States, the dispersal of the whole colony until only ten people were left. Then the return, the arrival of new immigrants from home, the first school (ah, he was proud of that!), the founding of a weekly newspaper, the appointment of a postmaster, the building of wooden houses, the new road to Winnipeg.

Every date the old man had noted down, and the number of houses in the villages every year, the names of the people. Here, for Tudni Thorsteinsen, was the foundation of a new nation, the record of a whole new race. In the village of wooden cottages, with the fish nets drying on the fences, he saw the beginning of something great. Now he hurried to set the record down before he died, so that the greatness of it would never be lost.

I left the patriarch of Gimli and walked down the main street. It was early spring, the ice too rotten to hold dogsleds, thick enough to keep the fishing boats at home. The young men were mending nets and tinkering with their boats by the shore, and I thought I could distinguish them, if I saw them again, from any other Canadians. They had a clean, lean look about them, and were as neat as their trim little town and of quiet, earnest expression. The girls, often blonde, were generally large and handsome. The whole place had an air of extraordinary cleanliness about it — people who had endured for a thousand years or more on a barren island in the Atlantic and counted themselves wealthy on this poor land by the lake side. At the drugstore Jean was drinking a milk shake and talking in English to some of the Gimli youngsters. The boys and girls talk English only. Canadians all.

Down the road towards Winnipeg — the road where old Thorsteinsen used to travel for two days by ox cart to get to town — we came upon a young man riding a bicycle. On the handle bars sat an aged woman with a scarlet kerchief over her head and a shawl about her shoulders. "Ukes," said the lady from Winnipeg, who was driving us. The square faces, flat noses, and high cheekbones showed their nationality. They had come in the great immigration from the Ukraine.

We stopped the car and offered the woman a lift, her son evidently being exhausted by the extra burden on his bicycle. She stood smiling at us shyly, a lined, bony face for an old master's brush. She could speak no word of English, but her son explained that she had been to church six miles up the road and he was bringing her back as far as his farm. She would have to walk six miles home.

She got into the car, grinning with pleasure, and settled herself into the back seat, rough hands folded, and at all our questions only smiled again and shook her head. Never would she learn the language or understand this country. Her hands told the story plainly enough. She was a beast of burden, and content.

When we came to her home, twelve miles from her church, she pointed at it excitedly, for fear we would pass by. We stopped and let her out at a huddle of squalid barns and a dirty-looking shack — queer contrast to the neat houses of the

Icelanders. She bowed to us and smiled again and trudged through the barnyard, up to the ankles in mud. She had not missed the weekly church services.

Closer to Winnipeg, on the east bank of the Red River, and opposite the original Scottish settlements, we could imagine we were in a foreign country. Bulbous church domes and twisted spires rose above the little poplar woods, the architecture of Byzantium, brought by long and tortuous passage into the prairies of Canada. The squat log houses were covered with white plaster and doors and window frames were painted blue or red. Exactly the same houses glisten white beside the Danube as you drive down through flocks of geese to Budapest.

There were glimpses here by the Red River — the white plastered houses, the church domes and cupolas, the women in scarlet kerchiefs and shapeless skirts — that could be moved bodily into central Europe and no one would know they had ever been away from it. A few of the more successful Ukrainian farmers had torn down their plastered houses or used them for barns, building new houses of Canadian style — universally hideous. They were beginning to learn the ways of the country.

In the railway station of Winnipeg you can still see the immigrants occasionally, their belongings done up in blankets and bed quilts, their children clustered around the women like scared chickens, but not many of them now.

In the spring of 1892 the station master of Winnipeg beheld two bearded men in woolly sheepskin coats who tried to speak to him, but could utter no word of English. They were Ivan Pilipinski and Vasil Leynak. They got jobs on a farm and in the autumn they disappeared. They had spied out the ground for their friends in Galicia and presently they returned with hundreds more like them. The great trek had started.

Forty years ago the stations from Montreal to the Rockies were crammed with these people — Sir Clifford Sifton's tide of settlement that built the prairies. The Men in Sheepskin Coats, as Sifton called them. For a time they would become the chief political and economic fact of Canada.

All over Europe Sifton searched them out and brought them here, regardless of blood or tradition. On the lonely sweep of the prairies they would cultivate the ground, said Sifton, raise crops, enrich Canada, and breed a new Canadian race. Time and soil and weather would wear down by erosion their separate characteristics and shape them to this country.

Out of the Ukraine they came and Galicia, out of Germany, Norway, Sweden, Holland, Poland, Italy, Austria, and the Balkans.

The meeting of these elements in the crucible of Canada is not as rapid as might be supposed. The French are confined mostly to Quebec, though they have spread lately into Northern Ontario, New Brunswick, and the Prairies. Of the other continental European stocks, 60 percent are on the prairies, living often in their own communities, little isolated clots of foreign blood not readily absorbed. Yet so wide-spread is the penetration of these strains that you will come upon a Ukrainian church, with mosquelike dome, on the hill above the Niagara shelf. You will find Russian peasants chanting their hymns by a wild river in the Canadian Rockies, a German family putting down its winter barrel of pigs' knuckles and sauerkraut in Kitchener, Ontario, an old Chinese vegetable grower smoking his pipe in the Dry Belt of British Columbia.

A Canadian Mosaic, John Murray Gibbon called this mixture of bloods, in his fine study of our people. Most Canadians do not attempt to understand these other races. They are peasants labouring by the roadside, or a Ukrainian kitchen maid to do the heavy work of the household, or that perennial nuisance, the naked Doukhobor, or the Oriental Problem. Only a few men like Gibbon have troubled to investigate these strange, inarticulate, shy people, have encouraged them to develop their native arts and handicrafts, their music and dances, to enrich the Mosaic of Canada.

From the United States we received our first immigrants in the United Empire Loyalist tide of Anglo-Saxon people, and its successive waves out of the American prairies. The English, next to the French, have been our largest strain, coming direct and by the American route. They and their descendants have no special home, being everywhere in our country. The accent of Oxford and of East London is heard from coast to coast, never dying this side of the grave.

The first generation of English, especially the gentry, usually keep their ways and often their clothes. You can see them growing fruit in the Okanagan, fishing for salmon at Cowichan, directing companies in our cities, or living on . . . remittances from home, without a complaint, in lonely homesteads among the mountains. The gentry will wear tweed coats from a West End tailor and the unmistakable look of Bond Street. They are handsome of face, charming of manner, sportsmen all, maintaining civilization in the wilderness and as the Englishman does everywhere, organizing society, entering public service, and labouring in charitable enterprises with a stern sense of obligation.

Their sons show no trace of England and have little knowledge of it, and without a new supply of English immigrants the old English flavour of Canada will be doomed.

From Scotland came the next wave of settlement and washed clear to the Pacific when Mackenzie reached the salt water on foot and Fraser's flimsy canoe foundered through the unknown torrent of Hell's Gate. Everywhere the Scottish people have succeeded, in city, in village, on lonely farm, and in Indian trading post, until you cannot mark their special place in Canada. You cannot go anywhere without finding them. So many of us still feel their blood that Canadian soldiers often prefer kilts to trousers, and the pipes skirling on a Canadian street as the troops march by will set all our hearts thumping.

In the village of Quesnel, British Columbia, four hundred miles up the Fraser, I have seen a Scottish piper leading a parade of cowboys and Indians to a rodeo and no one considered him or his music out of place. A friend of mine camped last year on a forgotten lake in the outer wilds of Ontario and was awakened by a strange sound to observe a Scotsman, in kilts, playing his pipes sadly beside the water, merely because he enjoyed the old music and the old memories.

Since Hugh McQuarters fired the cannon which killed Montgomery in the mean street of Lower Town, since the disbanding of the Scottish regiments and their marriage with the pretty French girls (who bore them children with Scottish names and no language but French), since the days of the starving settlers on the Red River, the Scots have claimed a large share of Canada. No one grudges it to them. Three generations removed from the old land, we still in dreams behold the Hebrides.

We are Irish, too. Out of Ireland's famines came many of our ancestors and there were more of them than Scots at the time of Confederation. Always the Irish were great breeders and great people to stick together. Only an Irishman like Thomas Talbot could have conceived such a fantastic settlement as Port Talbot, Ontario, where, in his castle of Malahide, like an eagle's nest in a cliff, this dashing soldier cooked, milked, farmed, baptized the babies, married the young folks, read the Sunday services, and made sure everyone came to church by sending a bottle of whisky around after the services. We have had other great Irishmen in Canada — Baldwin, the real father of popular government, Edward Blake, our finest legal mind, D'Arcy McGee, the poet and darling of Confederation, who was murdered by the Fenians for his love of Canada, Thomas Shaughnessy, the railway builder.

The Germans have come here steadily from the earliest times. In 1750 the English King acquired 300 settlers in Germany and sent them to Halifax, where their first settlement is still known as Dutch village. They were soon moved to Lunenberg and there they have remained German by race but Canadian by conviction. More Germans came up from the States with the Loyalists, and in Dundas County, Ontario, were settled as a buffer between the French Catholics and English

Protestants. In all directions their fat farms spread, with toil and thrift and understanding of the soil. Even their names have taken on Canadian sounds. Kountz became Coons, van Keugh is now Cook; and Merckle is Merkley.

Berlin, Ontario, which became Kitchener in the first World War, is a manufacturing city of importance, and I have heard a member of Parliament from there — pure German by breeding and looks — crying out in sincere agony of soul to the House of Commons for a larger army to fight Hitler. On the prairies are later German settlements, many of them grown up between the wars, when we thought Germans the most desirable immigrants from the Continent of Europe. Many of them are loyal to Canada.

On the farms, in the mines and the lumber camps, you will find the Swedes, Norwegians, and Finns — prodigious workers — and on the prairie land the Russians, with their strange churches, their peasant women and chunky daughters, their love of pageantry and song. The Italian labourers built a large part of our railways. The Jews have their own districts in large cities like Montreal.

So they came, swarming through our railway stations, the whiskered men in sheepskin coats, the tired women with bundles, the scared children, each of the Ukrainians with a handful of the Ukraine earth wrapped in a handkerchief, to be thrown into his grave. We saw them for a moment, trudging through the stations, crammed into the stinking colonist cars, then disappearing into the immensity of the prairies. Sometimes we saw them standing in their fields by the railways, gazing at us stolidly as the train passed, or their women working barefoot among the vegetables, outlined against the flat horizon. When they appeared timidly at concerts and village fairs to sing their folk songs and perform their lively dances, we were amazed. Why, these people actually knew something, knew things that we had forgotten or had never learned! And presently we saw their daughters marrying Canadian boys, who were glad to get them, and a pure-bred Icelander became Minister of War Services in the middle of our greatest war.

We heard their strange names — Ruthenians, Galicians, Ukrainians, Jugo-Slavs, Rumanians, Bulgarians — and we called them Bohunks or, if they were swarthy, we called them Wops.

Many strange people, beyond our comprehension, have come to us in this tide. Out of Pennsylvania early in the nineteenth century came the Russian Mennonites, followers of Menno Simons, strict pacifists and great farmers. Their scattered settlements stretch to the Pacific Coast, and you will find them living among the giant fir stumps of Vancouver Island, where Canadians failed to make a living. They brought the flax into the Red River country, they paid back their settlement loans to the government, and some went to Mexico because they would not send their children to Canadian schools. More came to Canada after the first World War, terrified of the Bolsheviks. A hundred thousand of them are farming here now.

The Moravian followers of John Hus came from the States a hundred and fifty years ago and there are still settlements of them near Edmonton. But strangest of all are the Doukhobors.

These are the Spirit Wrestlers, who left Russia to be free to worship God in their own way, to wait for the coming of Christ. So soon was He expected to arrive that they marched chanting through the prairie snow, stark naked, to meet Him. The tale of their wrestling with the spirits and with the police when they became unruly, their settlements, their quarrels, desertions, betrayals has been recognized at last as a minor epic and set down in a fine book by James Wright, a young Canadian. *Slava Bohu* he called his history — the Doukhobors' family greeting, which means "God be with you."

What agony the Wrestlers have suffered for the Spirit, marching naked through the snow of winter and the summer heat, locked up in foul jails by bewildered constabulary, who couldn't persuade them to put on their clothes, burning school houses, imprisoned on a lonely island in the sea because they would not send their children to school, defying the laws of Canada as stubbornly and dumbly as cattle! . . .

Yet Canadians from the earliest days have wanted more population, have built their towns, railways, and public services to serve more population, and require more population to carry the load of taxes. Always immigration has been accepted as a basic need in Canada, a constant policy, and its interruption was regarded solely as an emergency until the Depression ended. We know instinctively that more people must come here, that we cannot forever hold so much of the world's surface and so much of its wealth unused.

The Wheat-Land

Mary Weekes

Esther sat on the tongue of the waggon, reading her English mail. What jolly letters the girls wrote! This one now, from Lena, full of chit-chat about her latest party. And this, from Janet who had become stodgy from living in Bagdad. "The heat," Janet wrote complainingly, "is intolerable. Will thinks I should have a summer in England, but the thought of travelling with children and Arab servants sets me all of a dither." Both sisters asked her to let them have pictures of her ranch. Heigh-ho!

Esther looked about her. What was there to photograph? The shack, a flat-roofed affair of two rooms; two red grain elevators that stood out of the mirage tall and thin; a clump of wind-racked poplars in a muddy slough; warmish brown stacks of weathered straw, and crows that swooped upon the young of gophers, carrying them to their nests in the poplars. There was a decent barn, to be sure, but around and beyond that — nothing. Only fields of yellowing wheat running away, under a sky of china blue, unending.

The hot July sun beat down. Out of the silence the rich notes of nesting larks mingled with and drowned the harsh caw-caw of crows. But Esther did not hear. Her questing eye had found and was following Joe down the long black furrows. She watched his disc tear up the honey-colored stubble and turn the field into a melancholy brown. No! There was nothing to photograph.

It was nearing noon. Esther picked up her letters. The papers, she would keep for the loneliness of night-fall: It was then that the dirge of the coyotes, the demoniacal wail of the loons, and the screech of the owls ripped the silence of the long black night; it was then that the wind-borne soil beat its ghastly tattoo upon her window.

Unnoticed by Esther summer slipped into November. What a batch of English mail! Janet, grown tired now of the drab English climate, longed, she wrote, for the color and warmth of India. Lena, "fed up" with her holiday in Scotland, was all "nerves" and craved a change.

Esther threw down the letters, saddled Tim, and went for a run. The pony leaped over badger holes, almost throwing her. She galloped over stubble, raising in her flight prairie chicken, canvas backs, and mallards. She raced past over-flowing granaries and glistening stacks of new-piled straw. Purple earth flung away from her pony's feet. Tim was all afoam, but Esther's goal was the patch of color that ringed the distant slough.

There she dismounted and slapped down the reins. What alchemist had turned this dull colored prairie into an artist's palette? Purpled the willow withes, sent a reddening stream through the wild rose shoots, and let bronze creep into the goldenrod that spattered the trail? Ah! She must send a picture of her wheat-fields to Janet in colorful India; to Lena amongst her neat garden flowers.

We Didn't Know What a Mosquito Was

Barry Broadfoot

The thing I will always remember were the mosquitoes. They seemed to be so much bigger. So much more eager to bite you than today. I don't know, maybe it is this stuff they spray on the sloughs that make them less.

When I was a little girl we homesteaded on the prairie east of Calgary near the Saskatchewan border, and it was a country of more sloughs than it has now. Of course in Sweden we never knew what mosquitoes were. If you'd asked us what a mosquito was, we would have looked at you silly. They never told anyone there would be these creatures who would blind you and make the horses go mad, and that they were with you for three months. I'm talking about the pretty pamphlets with all the high-falutin' words and descriptions of the country that made it sound like paradise, something like out of the Smith Family Robinson. They never told my dad when he went to sign up for the trip. From what I found out, they never told him anything. Or anybody anything.

But you just could not believe what the mosquitoes were like. My mother would send me to the slough for a pail of water. The way was through thick grass. Long grass and this is where the mosquitoes lived. You'd be wearing a long skirt and long stockings, so it was your face and your neck and your hands you had to hide. Imagine going out in June in the warm morning wearing mittens to get a pail of water. That was what it was like. You wore a mosquito netting for your face and it wasn't until a month or so that the storekeeper mentioned he had got another order of mosquito netting. Then Dad found out there was such stuff.

That first summer when my father was plowing, I had to walk on one side of the horses and my smaller sister on the other waving cloths. Bits of cloth tied to sticks to keep the horses calm enough because the mosquitoes were driving them out of their minds. To distraction. It was a common sight to see a team with three people around it, one man plowing and two others brushing off. This went on, you understand, day after day. Yes, week after week, until the time came along in summer when all of a sudden there would be less of them and soon there would be none. They'd all died.

It was funny too. Some people the mosquitoes just did not bother. I've seen a man with his sleeves rolled up and his arms black with the nasty things and yet not one would be sucking blood, not one biting, and all the rest of us would be all done up.

Many the time I've heard neighbors sitting around our stove and they'd be talking about how bad things were. And I've often heard these men say that if they had to do it again, they'd go to where there were no mosquitoes. If there is such a place.

Where He Guides the Tractor

James M. Moir

Where he guides the tractor
in the field,
necessity marks the way for him.
Dust rises there
insubstantial as hope.

Through the long day
the wind
moves with him.
Overhead, clouds foretell a future
he cannot see.
Tomorrow is not his;
he is tomorrow's.

The harsh power
and sweep of this land
leaves no place for dreaming,
except in the small space
where the farm wife has created
a refuge of flowers.

At supper their words are few.
They speak of "this crop" and "next year",
their faces mask-like,
their faith wavering.

The wind ceases.
The huge night takes the prairie.
He turns from the darkened window;
he does not speak.

Mother Saved the Homestead

Barry Broadfoot

I remember that morning as if it were yesterday. I was five years old, this was in 1909, October, and my mother had sent me out to play and look after my sister Mary, who was three, almost four, and my little brother Colin, who was not quite two. I remember watching my father and my uncle ride away on horses across the prairie to help a neighbor fix up his house for winter. Everybody helped everybody else every way they could in those days and where we lived, the whole area was virgin prairie, around Hannah. The pioneers who came in that spring and lived in tents were now starting to finish their sod houses and get them ready to move into for winter.

So that left Mother alone looking after us three kids and my cousin and grandfather, who was in bed in the house, sick after a stroke. And to top it all off, my mother was pregnant. This was like it was on the prairie in those days. Women had to do a lot.

It was a queer morning, I remember — unreasonable warm. It was getting darker and there were more gusts of wind, and this to us meant a storm coming. It was about noon when a very bad swirl of wind struck us, and this time we could smell the odor of burning prairie wool. That was what we called the kind of grass that grew everywhere on the prairie. And then I looked to the southwest and I ran to the house as fast as I could yelling, "Fire! Fire!"

If you looked to the southwest you could see this ridge of grayish-black cloud, which was rising rapidly and spreading fast, and through it you could see the occasional finger of red shooting up into the cloud.

Mother grabbed up some blankets and herded us all toward the well, which was inside the fire guard that my dad had plowed. Just about the first thing a settler did was plow a fire guard to protect his homestead and family against these fires. So Mother took us to the well where the horse trough was and she sopped all the blankets. Then she said, "Whatever happens, make the children stay right here. The grass is worn off, so it won't burn. Wrap one blanket around each child."

Then she grabbed up another blanket and a pail of water and went to try and stop the fire. One woman and one blanket against that terrible fire, which by now we could see was made up of great flames, and as it got closer it made a tremendous noise, crackling and popping through the high grass as it came closer and closer to the fire guard, and there was my mother out there, doing somehow what she could to save the house. Remember my grandfather was in it because he was paralyzed, or partly paralyzed, and couldn't get out of bed.

The little kids were pretty good because they were used to me bossing them around, and under this black smoke which filled the sky we just huddled there in the wet blankets, trying to get breaths of air with all that smoke around. And then it was over. The fire had gone past around us and we heard my father's voice calling my name. Oh, it was a blessed sound.

I found out that the men had ridden over from the other house over all the fresh-burned earth and found Mother exhausted but still fighting the fire where it persisted in creeping under the sod of the fire guard, putting out all the flames before they could start moving toward the house where Grandpa was.

That is my memory of a prairie fire.

A Winter in the Lost Horse Hills

R. L. Gibson

Old timers will remember that the summer of 1889, was one of the hottest and dryest summers ever experienced in old Assiniboia. I can remember day after day, those sizzling heat waves we could see rising in the distance. Father used to say, "I believe that heat is coming straight up from the Gulf of Mexico." Not a blade of grass grew that summer. I can remember the ground around the door would fairly burn my bare feet. Many were the anxious inquiries among the settlers, "What's to be done for feed?"

We had four hundred sheep and quite a herd of cattle and horses. About the first of July a council of action was called among the few living just north of where Alameda now stands. My brother and two neighbours were delegated to go on a trip of discovery — food was cooked and prepared to last for at least two weeks. They decided to go north towards the Moose Mountains, but they found that all the hay lands were taken up in the mountains, north of Carlyle and along the west, so they rounded through the Gapview pass west of where George Smith was settler, Percy Post Office in those days. Matt Morrison was on the Moose Creek and had a shack up. They continued up the

Creek until they came to a hay marsh just north of the Lost Horse Hills. The hay was splendid, and I suppose it grows there to this day, broad leaf in big tufts among the moss.

They dug a small well on the Creek about one and a half miles south of the Hills where the camp was situated. They found frost at two feet in sinking this shallow well; there was about six inches of dry grass that protected it from the hot sun. This was about all they did before returning home to report the find. They got everything ready to return to cut and stack the hay which they completed about the middle of August. The party then returned again to Alameda.

Buildings had to be put up so Mr. John Truscott and I went to erect the sod buildings. We completed this in thirty days. We built a large sheep shed, two stables 30′ x 50′, and also put up a large sod shack. I was seventeen years old then and they wondered if I would stand the heavy work. I kept my end up. We had to go to a large ravine about four or five miles east or northeast for poles to roof with. In this coulee many buffalo had been killed as many bones and skulls were lying in the bottom of the ravine in wild profusion. Apparently the buffalo had been driven over the steep banks and shot as this was a favorite way to do it.

We completed the building November first and left to notify them at Alameda that all was ready for winter. The return trip with the cattle was quite tedious but eventually we got all the stock safely to winter quarters. My mother, father, sister Josie, my brother Porter, Mr. William T. A. Deyell and myself composed the wintering party.

We got settled in our quarters nicely for winter. We had a good supply of meat that winter, having had to kill all our poultry — ducks, turkeys and chickens — also hogs. The stock did well and put on flesh as the hay was the best prairie hay I ever saw, the milk was like off fresh grass and the butter a lovely dark orange.

We went through the usual routine of ranch life. We dug a

well sixteen feet deep and had the finest water possible to find in the country — an abundance of it. Along about the middle of January we caught one hundred and eighty-seven pike, in a spring down the creek from where the camp was situated. This was a fine addition to our supply of meats. About this time also we saw a herd of twenty-two deer one sunny day moving along the contour of the hills. We went hunting that afternoon and bagged two. That winter we got seven altogether. You can imagine how well we were fed with seven kinds of meat to choose from as follows: beef, pork, ducks, turkey, chicken, fish and venison. Could a king ask for better? My mother was a lavish cook and did we enjoy our meals out in the wilds!

Only one person called on us all winter, that was Sam Hopper of Arcola. He drove up in a jumper about the middle of December.

To make a long story short, winter passed quite swiftly away. We had one awful storm on the ninth of February, 1890, one of those ones which come up with the swiftness of a hurricane. Porter was down at the spring where we caught the fish, watering the cattle. We all thought, "he's a gonner," but he was a wise kid, only fourteen years old. He grabbed a cow's tail and hung on. The cattle led him back to the buildings.

Well, spring came and all the rest of the party went back to Alameda with the horses and cattle. My brother Porter and I stayed to keep the sheep till the roads permitted us to go home. During the month or five weeks we stayed behind, we made many trips to the Lost Horse Hills. The hills had a fascination, so one bright day found us on top of the large round butte on the west end, a noble pile of earth. While looking around I spied a burned match and I turned to Porter and said, "Someone has been here and the only thing that would bring them here would be hunting horses." I said, "Let's name these hills the 'Lost Horse Hills.' " We gathered rocks and printed out the name and the date, April 1890. We used to go up there to see if we could spot any living thing, anything human. We were lonesome to see someone during those days of isolation, but we never saw a living soul. It was solitude indeed, and I can feel that feeling now, so still, just as nature made it. The hill was used by Indians for long ages as a lookout post.

Well, we pulled out for home on May 1st, 1890, with about four hundred sheep. I think those were the first sheep ever brought into Saskatchewan. We had a slow, nerve-wracking trip and arrived home May the 10th. Little lambs were coming into the world the last two days of our journey so we had to deposit them in boxes and boilers along the wagon. Mother said, "Well, a lamb in every nook and corner!"

That was the winter of the Russian Flu. It went everywhere, but we all escaped at Lost Horse Hills. It just didn't know we were up there!

Still Stands the House

Gwen Pharis Ringwood

The icy wind of a northern blizzard sweeps across the prairie, lashes about the old Warren farmhouse, and howls insistently at the door and windows. But the Warren house was built to withstand the menace of the Canadian winter and scornfully suffers the storm to shriek about the chimney corner, to knock at the door and rattle the windows in a wild attempt to force an entrance.

The living room of this house has about it a faded austerity, a decayed elegance that is as remote and cheerless as a hearth in which no fire is ever laid. The room has made a stern and solemn pact with the past. Once it held the warm surge of life; but as the years have gone by, it has settled in a rigid pattern of neat, uncompromising severity.

As if in defiance of the room, the frost has covered the window in the rear wall with a wild and exotic design. Beside the window is an imposing leather armchair, turned toward the handsome coal stove in the right corner. A footstool is near the chair. A door at the centre of the rear wall leads to the snow-sheeted world outside. Along the left wall, between a closed door to a bedroom (now unused) and an open door to the kitchen, is a mahogany sideboard. Above it is a portrait of old Martin Warren, who built this house and lived in it until his death. The portrait is of a stern and handsome man in his early fifties, and in the expression of the eyes the artist has caught something of his unconquerable will.

An open staircase, winding to the bedrooms upstairs, extends into the room at right. There is a rocking chair by the stove with a small stand-table beside it. A mahogany dining table and two matching chairs are placed at a convenient distance from the sideboard and the kitchen door. The figured wall paper is cracked and faded. The dark rug, the heavy curtains, and the tablecloth show signs of much wear, but there is nothing of cheapness about them.

Two coal oil lanterns have been left beside the kitchen door. Blooming bravely on the table, in contrast to its surroundings, is a pot of lavender hyacinths.

RUTH WARREN, *is standing near the outside door, talking to* ARTHUR MANNING, *who is about to leave.* RUTH *is small, fair-haired, and pretty, twenty-five or twenty-six years of age. There is more strength in her than her rather delicate appearance would indicate. She wears a soft blue house-dress with a light wool cardigan over it.*

MANNING *is a middle-aged man of prosperous appearance. He wears a heavy overcoat over a dark business suit. His hat, gloves and scarf are on the armchair.*

RUTH Do you think you'd better try to go back tonight, Mr. Manning? The roads may be drifted.

MANNING It's a bad blizzard, all right, but I don't think I'll have any trouble. There's a heater in the car, and I've just had the engine checked over.

RUTH — You'll be welcome if you care to spend the night.

MANNING — Thank you, but I'm afraid I've got to get back to town. I'd hate to try it in an old car, but this one of mine can pull through anything.

RUTH — I've never seen a storm come up so quickly.

MANNING — These prairie blizzards are no joke. One of my sheepherders got lost in one last year, just half a mile from the house. He froze to death out there trying to find his way.

RUTH — How frightful!

MANNING — One of the ranch hands found him the next morning. Poor fellow — he'd herded for me for twenty years. I never knew how he came to be out in a storm like that.

RUTH — They say when a person gets lost he begins to go round in a circle, although it seems straight ahead.

MANNING — Yes, I've always heard that. The winters are the one thing I've got against this country.

RUTH — *(wistfully):* I used to like them in town. We went skating on the river and tobogganing. But out here it's different.

MANNING — If Bruce sells the farm and takes this irrigated place near town, you won't notice the winter so much, Mrs. Warren.

RUTH — No. I hope he does take your offer, Mr. Manning. I want him to.

MANNING — He'll never get a better. Five thousand dollars and an irrigated quarter is a good price for a dry-land farm these days.

RUTH — If only we didn't have to decide so soon.

MANNING I talked it all over with Bruce in town a couple of weeks ago, and I think he's pretty well made up his mind. All he needs to do is sign the papers.

RUTH I thought he'd have until spring to decide.

MANNING I've got orders to close the deal before I go South next week. You tell Bruce I'll come by tomorrow or the next day, and we can get it all settled.

RUTH I'll tell him. I hope he does take it, Mr. Manning.

MANNING I know you do and you're right. I think all he needs is a little persuading. He's had a hard time here these dry years.

RUTH I don't know what Hester will say.

MANNING I understand she's very much attached to the place. It is true that she never leaves the farm?

RUTH Not often.

MANNING She'd be better off where she could get out more.

RUTH I don't know.

MANNING I suppose all those years out here, keeping house for Bruce and her father, were pretty hard on her.

RUTH The house has come to mean so much to her. But maybe she won't mind. (*Smiling hopefully.*) We'll see.

The door to the bedroom, left, is opened quickly, and HESTER WARREN *enters the room. She closes and locks the door behind her and stands looking at the two in the room with cold surmise.* HESTER *is forty years old. She is tall, dark and unsmiling. The stern rigidity of her body, the bitter austerity of her mouth, and the almost arrogant dignity of her carriage seem to make her a part of the room she enters. There is bitter resentment in her dark eyes as she confronts* RUTH *and* MANNING. *She holds a leather-bound Bible close to her breast.*

RUTH *(startled):* Why, Hester! I thought you never unlocked that door.

HESTER *(quietly):* No. I keep Father's room as it was.

RUTH Then why were you —

HESTER I was reading in Father's room. I heard a stranger.

RUTH You know Mr. Manning, Hester.

MANNING *(with forced friendliness):* I don't suppose you remember me, Miss Warren.

HESTER *(without moving):* How do you do?

MANNING *(embarrassed at her coldness and anxious to get away):* Well, I'll be getting on home. I'll leave these papers for Bruce to sign, Mrs. Warren. Tell him I'll come by tomorrow. He'll find it's all there, just as we talked about it. *(He lays the document on the table.)*

RUTH Thank you, Mr. Manning.

MANNING *(turning to go):* Take care of yourselves. Goodnight. *(To* HESTER) Goodnight, Miss Warren. (HESTER *barely nods.)*

RUTH You're sure you ought to try it in the storm?

MANNING Sure. There's no danger if I go right away. *(He goes out.)*

RUTH *(calling after him as she shuts the door):* Goodnight.

(HESTER *watches* MANNING *out and, as* RUTH *returns, she looks at her suspiciously. There is a silence which* HESTER *finally breaks.)*

HESTER What did he want here?

RUTH *(uncomfortable under* HESTER'S *scrutiny):* He just left some papers for Bruce to look over,

Hester. He was in a hurry so he didn't wait to see Bruce.

HESTER I see. What has Arthur Manning got to do with Bruce?

RUTH It's something to do with the farm, Hester. I'll put these away. *(She starts to take up the document on the table, but* HESTER *is before her.)*

HESTER *(after a long look at the document):* A deed of sale. *(Turning angrily upon* RUTH.) So this is what you've been hiding from me.

RUTH *(quickly):* Oh, no! Nothing's settled, Hester. Mr. Manning made an offer, and Bruce wants to think it over. That's all.

HESTER *(her eyes betraying her intense agitation):* Bruce isn't going to sell this place!

RUTH It's just an offer. Nothing has been decided.

HESTER Your hand's in this! You've been after him to leave here.

RUTH *(trying to conciliate her):* Let's not quarrel. You can talk to Bruce about it, Hester.

HESTER You hate this house, I know that.

RUTH No. *(Facing* HESTER *firmly.)* But I think Bruce ought to sell.

HESTER You married him. You made your choice.

RUTH *(quietly):* I've not regretted that. It's just that we're so cut off and lonely here, and this is the best offer we could get. But let me put these away. *(Indicating the deed of sale.)* We'll talk about it later, the three of us.

HESTER *(allowing* RUTH *to take the papers):* You may as well burn them. He isn't going to sell.

RUTH Please, Hester . . . we'll discuss it when Bruce comes. *(She places the document on the sideboard, then crosses to the stove.)* I'll build up the fire.

(HESTER *takes the Bible to the sideboard and places it under her father's portrait. She stands looking up at the portrait.)*

HESTER This house will not be sold. I won't allow it.

(RUTH *puts some coal on the fire.)*

RUTH *(shivering):* It's so cold it almost frightens me. The thermometer has dropped ten degrees within the hour.

HESTER: I hope Bruce knows enough to get the stock in. They'll freeze where they stand if they're left out tonight. *(She moves to the window and takes her knitting from the ledge.)*

RUTH: He'll have them in. *(Crossing to the table.)* Look, Hester, how the hyacinths have bloomed. I could smell them when I came in the room just now.

HESTER: Hyacinths always seem like death to me.

RUTH *(her voice is young and vibrant):* Oh, no. They're birth, they're spring! They say in Greece you find them growing wild in April. *(She takes an old Wedgwood bowl from the sideboard, preparing to set the pot of hyacinths in it.)*

HESTER *(in a dry, unfriendly tone):* I've asked you not to use that Wedgwood bowl. It was my grandmother's. I don't want it broken.

RUTH I'm sorry. *(Replacing the bowl, she gets a plain one from inside the sideboard.)* I thought the hyacinths would look so pretty in it, but I'll use the plain one.

HESTER You've gone to as much trouble for that plant as if it were a child.

(HESTER *sits in the rocking chair by the stove.)*

RUTH *(placing the hyacinths in the bowl):* They're so sweet. I like to touch them.

HESTER They'll freeze tonight, I'm thinking.

RUTH Not in here. We'll have to keep the fire up anyway. *(Leaving the bowl of hyacinths on the table,* RUTH *returns to the sideboard, taking some bright chintz from the drawer. She holds it up for* HESTER *to see.)* I've almost finished the curtains, Hester.

HESTER *(tonelessly):* You have?

RUTH Don't you think they'll make this room more cheerful?

HESTER The ones we have seem good enough to me.

RUTH But they're so old.

HESTER *(coldly):* Old things have beauty when you've eyes to see it. That velvet has a richness that you can't buy now.

RUTH *(moving to the window):* I want to make the room gay and happy for the spring. You'll see how much difference these will make.

HESTER I've no doubt.

(HESTER *rises and goes to the table to avoid looking at the curtain.)*

RUTH *(measuring the chintz with the curtains at the window):* I wonder if I have them wide enough. *(The wind rises. As if the sound had quelled her pleasure in the bright curtains,* RUTH *turns slowly away from the window. A touch of hysteria creeps into her voice.)* The wind swirls and shrieks and raises such queer echoes in this old house! It seems to laugh at us in here, thinking we're safe, hugging the stove! As if it knew it could blow out the light and the fire and . . . *(Getting hold of herself.)* I've never seen a blizzard when it was as cold as this. Have you, Hester?

HESTER *(knitting):* Bruce was born on a night like this.

(Throughout this scene HESTER *seldom looks at* RUTH *but gives all her attention to her knitting. She seems reluctant to talk and yet impelled to do so.)*

RUTH I didn't know.

HESTER Father had to ride for the doctor while I stayed here with mother.

RUTH Alone?

HESTER Yes. I was rubbing father's hand with snow when he heard the baby crying. Then we helped the doctor bathe him.

RUTH You were such a little girl to do so much.

HESTER After mother died I did it all.

RUTH I know, but it was too hard for a child. I don't see how you managed.

HESTER Father always helped me with the washing.

RUTH Not many men would stay in from the field to do that.

HESTER No. *(Her knitting drops to her lap, and for a moment she is lost in the past.)* "We'll have to lean on one another now, daughter." . . . Those were his words . . . And that's the way it was. I was beside him until — I never left him.

RUTH *(at* HESTER's *side):* You've never talked of him like this before.

HESTER *(unconscious of* RUTH*):* He always liked the snow. *(Her eyes are on the portrait of her father.)* He called it a moving shroud, a winding sheet that the wind lifts and raises and lets fall again.

RUTH It is like that.

HESTER He'd come in and say. "The snow lies deep on the summer fallow, Hester. That means a good crop next year."

RUTH I know. It's glorious in the fall with the wheat like gold on the hills. No wonder he loved it.

HESTER *(called out of her dream, she abruptly resumes her knitting):* There hasn't been much wheat out there these last years.

RUTH That isn't Bruce's fault, Hester.

HESTER You have to love a place to make things grow. The land knows when you don't care about it, and Bruce doesn't care about it any more. Not like father did.

RUTH *(her hands raised to touch the portrait above the sideboard):* I wish I'd known your father.

HESTER *(rising and facing* RUTH *with a sudden and terrible anger):* Don't touch that picture. It's mine.

RUTH *(startled, she faces* HESTER*):* Why, Hester —

HESTER Can't I have anything of my own? Must you put your fingers on everything I have?

RUTH *(moving to* HESTER*):* Hester, you know I didn't mean — What is the matter with you?

HESTER I won't have you touch it.

RUTH *(gently):* Do you hate my being here so much?

HESTER *(turning away):* You've more right here than I have now, I suppose.

RUTH *(crossing over to the stove):* You make me feel that I've no right at all.

HESTER *(a martyr now):* I'm sorry if you don't approve

my ways. I can go, if that's what you want.

RUTH *(pleading):* Please . . . I've never had a sister, and when Bruce told me he had one, I thought we'd be such friends . . .

HESTER *(sitting in the chair by the stove):* We're not a family to put words to everything we feel. *(She resumes her knitting.)*

RUTH *(trying to bridge the gulf between them):* I get too excited over things; I know it. Bruce tells me I sound affected when I say too much about the way I feel, the way I like people . . . or the sky in the evening. I —

HESTER *(without looking up):* Did you get the separator put up? Or shall I do it?

(Discouraged, RUTH *turns away, and going to the table, sits down with her sewing.)*

RUTH It's ready for the milk when Bruce brings it. I put it together this morning.

HESTER The lanterns are empty.

RUTH I'll fill them in a minute.

HESTER When I managed this house, I always filled the lanterns right after supper. Then they were ready.

RUTH *(impatiently):* I said I'd fill them, Hester, and I will. They're both there in the corner. *(She indicates the lanterns at the end of the sideboard.)*

HESTER Bruce didn't take one, then?

RUTH No.

HESTER You'd better put a lamp in the window.

(RUTH *lights a small lamp on the sideboard and takes it to the window.)*

RUTH I wish he'd come. It's strange how women feel safer when their men are near, close enough to touch, isn't it? No matter how strong you think you are. *(As she speaks,* RUTH *drapes some of the chintz over the armchair.)*

HESTER I can't say that I need any strength from Bruce, or could get it if I needed it.

RUTH That's because he's still a little boy to you. *(A pause. Then* RUTH *speaks hesitantly.)* Hester.

HESTER Yes?

RUTH Will you mind the baby in the house?

HESTER *(after a silence, constrainedly):* No, I won't mind. I'll keep out of the way.

RUTH *(warmly, commanding a response):* I don't want you to. You'll love him, Hester.

HESTER *(harshly):* I loved Bruce, but I got no thanks for it. He feels I stand in his way now.

RUTH *(suddenly aware that* HESTER *has needed and wanted love):* You mustn't say that. It isn't true.

HESTER When he was little, after mother died, he'd come tugging at my hand . . . He'd get hold of my little finger and say, "Come, Hettie . . . come and look." Everything was "Hettie" then.

RUTH *(eagerly, moving to* HESTER*):* It will be like that again. This baby will be almost like your own.

HESTER *(as if* RUTH's *words were an implied reproach):* I could have married, and married well if I'd had a mind to.

RUTH I know that. I've wondered why you didn't, Hester.

HESTER The young men used to ride over here on Sunday, but I stopped that. *(A pause.)* I never saw a man I'd let touch me. Maybe you don't mind that kind of thing. I do.

RUTH *(involuntarily; it is a cry):* No! *(Attempting to put her arms around* HESTER.*)* What hurt you?

HESTER *(rising):* Don't try your soft ways on me. *(She*

moves behind the armchair; her hands fall caressingly on the back of the chair.) I couldn't leave Bruce and father here alone. My duty was here in the house. So I stayed. (HESTER *notices the chintz material draped over the chair and taking it up, turns to* RUTH *angrily.)* What do you intend to do with this?

RUTH I thought . . . there's enough left to make covers for the chair to match the curtains —

HESTER *(throwing the chintz down):* This is father's chair. I won't have it changed.

RUTH I'm sorry, Hester. *(With spirit.)* Must we keep everything the same forever?

HESTER There's nothing in this house that isn't good, that wasn't bought with care and pride by one of us who loved it. This stuff is cheap and gaudy.

RUTH It isn't dull and falling apart with age.

HESTER Before my father died, when he was ill, he sat here in this chair where he could see them threshing from the window. It was the first time since he came here that he'd not been in the fields at harvest. Now you come — you who never knew him, who never saw him — and you won't rest until —

RUTH Hester!

HESTER You've got no right to touch it! *(Her hands grip the back of the old chair as she stands rigid, her eyes blazing.)*

BRUCE WARREN *enters from outside, carrying a pail of milk. He is tall and dark, about thirty years old, sensitive and bitter. His vain struggle to make the farm pay since his father's death has left him with an oppressive sense of failure. He is proud and quick to resent an imagined reproach. He has dark hair, his shoulders are a little stooped, and he moves restlessly and abruptly. Despite his moodiness, he is extremely likeable. He is dressed warmly in dark trousers, a sweater under his heavy leather coat; he wears gloves, cap and high boots. He brushes the snow from his coat as he enters.)*

BRUCE (*carrying the milk into the kitchen):* Is the separator up, Ruth?

RUTH Yes, it's all ready, Bruce. Wait, I'll help you. *(She follows him into the kitchen.)*

*(*HESTER *stands at the chair a moment after they have gone; her eyes fall on the plant on the table. Slowly she goes towards it, as if drawn by something she hated. She looks down at the lavender blooms for a moment. Then with a quick, angry gesture, she crushes one of the stalks. She turns away and is winding up her wool when* BRUCE *and* RUTH *return.)*

RUTH You must be frozen.

BRUCE *(taking off his coat and gloves):* I'm cold, all right. God, it's a blizzard: thirty-eight below, and a high wind. *(He throws his coat over a chair at the table.)*

RUTH *(with pride):* Did you see the hyacinths? They've bloomed since yesterday.

BRUCE *(smiling):* Yes, they're pretty. *(Touching them, he notices the broken stalk.)* Looks like one of them's broken.

RUTH Where? *(She sees it.)* Oh, it is! And that one hadn't bloomed yet! I wonder . . . It wasn't broken when I —

(RUTH *turns accusingly to* HESTER.) Hester!

(HESTER *returns* RUTH's *look calmly.)*

HESTER *(coldly):* Yes?

RUTH Hester, did you . . .

BRUCE *(going to the fire):* Oh, Ruth, don't make such a fuss about it. It can't be helped.

HESTER I'll take care of the milk. *(She takes the small lamp from the window.)*

RUTH I'll do it.

HESTER *(moving toward the kitchen):* You turn the separator so slow the cream's as thin as water.

RUTH *(stung to reply):* That's not true. You never give me a chance to —

BRUCE *(irritably):* For God's sake, don't quarrel about it. *(He sits in the chair by the stove.)*

HESTER I don't intend to quarrel. *(She goes into the kitchen.)*

*(*RUTH *follows* HESTER *to the door. The sound of the separator comes from the kitchen.* RUTH *turns wearily, takes up the pot of hyacinths, and places them on the stand near the stove. Then sits on the footstool.)*

RUTH It's always that way.

BRUCE *(gazing moodily at the stove):* Why don't you two try to get along? *(A silence.)*

RUTH Did you put the stock in? *(The question is merely something to fill the empty space of silence between them.)*

BRUCE Yes. That black mare may foal tonight. I'll have to look at her later on.

RUTH It's bitter weather for a little colt to be born.

BRUCE Yes.

(Another silence. Finally RUTH, *to throw off the tension between them, gets up and moves her footstool over to his chair.)*

RUTH I'm glad you're here. I've been lonesome for you.

BRUCE *(putting his hand on hers):* I'm glad to be here.

RUTH I thought of you out at the barn, trying to work in this cold.

BRUCE I was all right. I'd hate to walk far tonight, though. You can't see your hand before your face.

RUTH *(after a look at the kitchen):* Hester's been so strange again these last few days, Bruce.

BRUCE I know it's hard, Ruth.

RUTH It's like it was when I first came here. At everything I touch, she cries out like I'd hurt her somehow.

BRUCE Hester has to do things her own way. She's always been like that.

RUTH If only she could like me a little. I think she almost does sometimes, but then —

BRUCE You think too much about her.

RUTH Maybe it's because we've been shut in so close. I'm almost afraid of her lately.

BRUCE She's not had an easy life, Ruth.

RUTH I know that. She's talked about your father almost constantly today.

BRUCE His death hit us both hard. Dad ran the farm, decided everything.

RUTH It's been six years, Bruce.

BRUCE There are things you don't count out by years.

RUTH He wouldn't want you to go on remembering forever.

BRUCE *(looking at the floor):* No.

RUTH You should get free of this house. It's not good for you to stay here. It's not good for Hester. *(Getting up, she crosses to the sideboard and returns with the deed of sale, which she hands to* BRUCE.*)* Mr. Manning left this for you. He's coming back to-morrow for it, when you've signed it. *(He takes the papers.)*

BRUCE *(annoyed by her assurance):* He doesn't need to get so excited. I haven't decided to sign it yet. He said he wouldn't need to know till spring.

(He goes over to the lamp at the table and studies the document.)

RUTH His company gave him orders to close the deal this week or let it go.

BRUCE This week?

RUTH That's what he said.

BRUCE Well, I'll think about it.

RUTH You'll have to decide tonight, Bruce. No one else will offer you as much. Five thousand dollars and an irrigated farm a mile from town seems a good price.

BRUCE I'm not complaining about the deal. It's fair.

RUTH *(urgently):* You're going to take it, aren't you, Bruce?

BRUCE I don't know. God, I don't know. *(He throws the document on the table.)* I don't want to sell, Ruth. I think I'll try it another year.

RUTH Bruce, you've struggled here too long now. You haven't had a crop, a good crop, in five years.

BRUCE I need to be told that!

RUTH It's not your fault. But you've told me you ought to give it up, that it's too dry here.

BRUCE We may get a crop this year. We're due for one.

RUTH If you take this offer, we'll be nearer town. We'll have water on the place. We can have a garden, and trees growing.

BRUCE That's about what those irrigated farms are — gardens.

RUTH And, Bruce, it wouldn't be so lonely there, so cruelly lonely.

BRUCE I told you how it was before you came.

RUTH *(resenting his tone):* You didn't tell me you worshipped a house. That you made a god of a house and a section of land. You didn't tell me that!

BRUCE *(angrily):* You didn't tell me that you'd moon at

a window for your old friends, either. *(He stands up and throws the deed of sale on the table.)*

RUTH How could I help it here?

BRUCE And you didn't tell me you'd be afraid of having a child. What kind of a woman are you that you don't want your child?

RUTH That's not true.

BRUCE No? You cried when you knew, didn't you?

RUTH Bruce!

BRUCE *(going blindly on):* What makes you feel the way you do, then? Other women have children without so much fuss. Other women are glad.

RUTH *(intensely angry):* Don't speak to me like that. Keep your land. Eat and sleep and dream land, I don't care!

BRUCE *(turning to the portrait of his father):* My father came out here and took a homestead. He broke the prairie with one plough and a team of horses. He built a house to live in out of the sod. You didn't know that, did you? He and mother lived here in a sod shanty and struggled to make things grow. They built a one-roomed shack; and when the good years came, they built this house. The finest in the country! I thought my son would have it.

RUTH *(moving to him):* What is there left to give a son? A house that stirs with ghosts. A piece of worn-out land where the rain never comes.

BRUCE That's not all. I don't suppose you can understand.

RUTH *(turning away from him, deeply hurt):* No, I don't suppose I can. You give me little chance to know how you feel about things.

BRUCE *(his anger gone):* Ruth, I didn't mean that. But you've always lived in town. *(He goes to the window and stands looking out for a moment, then turns.)* Those rocks along the fence out there, I picked up every one of them with my own hands and carried them with my own hands across the field and piled them there. I've ploughed that southern slope along the coulee every year since I was twelve. *(His voice is torn with a kind of shame for his emotion.)* I feel about the land like Hester does about the house, I guess. I don't want to leave it. I don't want to give it up.

RUTH *(gently):* But it's poor land, Bruce.

(BRUCE *sits down, gazing gloomily at the fire.* HESTER *comes in from the kitchen with the small lamp and places it on the sideboard. Then she sits at the table, taking up her knitting. As* BRUCE *speaks, she watches him intently.)*

BRUCE Yes, it's strange that in a soil that won't grow trees a man can put roots down, but he can.

RUTH *(at his side):* You'd feel the same about another place, after a little while.

BRUCE I don't know. When I saw the wind last spring blowing the dirt away, the dirt I'd ploughed and harrowed and sowed to grain, I felt as though part of myself was blowing away in the dust. Even now, with the land three feet under snow, I can look out and feel it waiting for the seed I've saved for it.

RUTH But if we go, we'll be nearer other people, not cut off from everything that lives.

BRUCE You need people, don't you?

HESTER Yes. She needs them. I've seen her at the window looking toward the town. Day after day she stands there.

(BRUCE *and* RUTH, *absorbed in the conflict between them, had forgotten* HESTER'*s presence.*

At HESTER's *word,* RUTH *turns on them both, flaming with anger.)*

RUTH You two. You're so *perfect!*

HESTER *(knitting):* We could always stand alone, the three of us. We didn't need to turn to every stranger who held his hand out.

RUTH No! You'd sit here in this husk of a house, living like shadows, until these four walls closed in on you, buried you.

HESTER I never stood at a window, looking down the road that leads to town.

RUTH *(the pent-up hysteria of the day and the longing of months breaks through, tumbling out in her words):* It's not for myself I look down that road, Hester. It's for the child I'm going to have. You're right, Bruce, I am afraid. It's not what you think, though, not for myself. You two and your father lived so long in this dark house that you forgot there's a world beating outside, forgot that people laugh and play sometimes. And you've shut me out! *(There is a catch in her voice.)* I never would have trampled on your thoughts if you'd given them to me. But as it is, I might as well not be a person. You'd like a shadow better that wouldn't touch your house. A child would die here. A child can't live with shadows.

(Much disturbed, BRUCE *rises and goes to her.)*

BRUCE Ruth! I didn't know you hated it so much.

RUTH I thought it would change. I thought I could change it. You know now.

BRUCE *(quietly):* Yes.

RUTH *(pleading):* If we go, I'll *want* this child, Bruce. Don't you see? But I'm not happy here. What kind of a life will our child have? He'll be old before he's out of school. *(She looks at the hyacinth on the stand.)* He'll be like the hyacinth bud that's broken before it bloomed.

(BRUCE *goes to the table and stands looking down at the deed of sale. His voice is tired and flat, but resolved.)*

BRUCE All right. I'll tell Manning I'll let him have the place.

HESTER *(turning quickly to* BRUCE): What do you mean?

BRUCE I'm going to sell the farm to Manning. He was here today.

HESTER *(standing up, her eyes blazing):* You can't sell this house.

BRUCE *(looking at the deed of sale):* Oh, Ruth's right. We can't make a living on the place. *(He sits down, leafing through the document.)* It's too dry. And too far from school.

HESTER It wasn't too far for you to go, or me.

BRUCE *(irritably):* Do you think I want to sell?

HESTER *She* does. But she can't do it. *(Her voice is low.)* This house belongs to me.

BRUCE Hester, don't start that again! I wish to God the land had been divided differently, but it wasn't.

HESTER Father meant for us to stay here and keep things as they were when he was with us.

BRUCE The soil wasn't blowing away when he was farming it.

HESTER He meant for me to have the house.

RUTH You'll go with us where we go, Hester.

HESTER *(to* RUTH): You came here. You plotted with him to take this house from me. But it's mine!

BRUCE *(his voice cracks through the room):* Stop that, Hester! I love this place as much as you do, but

I'm selling it. I'm selling it, I tell you. *(As he speaks, he gets up abruptly and, taking up his coat, puts it on.)*

(HESTER sinks slowly into the chair, staring. RUTH *tries to put her hand on* BRUCE's *arm.)*

RUTH Bruce! Not that way! Not for me. If it's that way, I don't care enough.

BRUCE *(shaking himself free):* Oh, leave me alone!

RUTH Bruce!

BRUCE *(going to the door):* I'll be glad when it's over, I suppose.

RUTH Where are you going?

BRUCE *(taking his cap and gloves):* To look at the mare.

RUTH Bruce! *(But he has gone.)*

HESTER *(getting up, she goes to her father's chair and stands behind it, facing* RUTH, *she moves and speaks as if she were in a dream):* This is my house. I won't have strangers in it.

RUTH *(at the table, without looking at* HESTER*):* Oh, Hester! I didn't want it to be this way. I tried —

HESTER *(as if she were speaking to a stranger):* Why did you come here?

RUTH I've hurt you. But I'm right about this. I know I'm right.

HESTER There isn't any room for you.

RUTH Can't you see? It's for all of us.

(HESTER *comes toward* RUTH *with a strange, blazing anger in her face.)*

HESTER I know your kind. You tempted him with your bright hair.

RUTH Hester!

HESTER Your body anointed with jasmine for his pleasure.

RUTH Hester, don't say such things!

HESTER Oh, I know what you are! You and women like you. You put a dream around him with your arms, a sinful dream.

RUTH *(drawing back):* Hester!

HESTER You lift your white face to every stranger like you offered him a cup to drink from. *(Turning from* RUTH, *as if she had forgotten her presence,* HESTER *looks fondly at the room.)* I'll never leave this house.

(BRUCE *opens the door and comes in quickly and stormily. He goes into the kitchen as he speaks.)*

BRUCE That mare's got out. She jumped the corral. I'll have to go after her.

RUTH *(concerned):* Bruce, where will she be?

BRUCE *(returning with an old blanket):* She'll be in the snowshed by the coulee. She always goes there when she's about to foal.

(HESTER *sits in the chair by the stove, her knitting in her hand. She pays no attention to the others.)*

RUTH But you can't go after her in this storm.

BRUCE I'll take this old blanket to cover the colt, if it's born yet. Where's the lantern? *(He sees the two lanterns by the kitchen door and, taking one of them to the table, lights it.)*

RUTH It's three miles, Bruce. You mustn't go on foot. It's dangerous.

BRUCE I'll have to. She'd never live through the night, or the colt either. *(He turns to go.)* You'd better go to bed. Goodnight, Hester.

RUTH Let me come with you.

BRUCE No. *(Then, as he looks at her, all resentment leaves him. He puts down the lantern, goes to her, and takes her in his arms.)* Ruth, forget what I said. You know I didn't mean —

RUTH *(softly):* I said things I didn't mean, too —

BRUCE I love you, Ruth. You know it, don't you?

RUTH Bruce! *(He kisses her, and for a moment their love is a flame in the room.)*

BRUCE Don't worry. I won't be long.

RUTH I'll wait.

(BRUCE *goes out.* RUTH *follows him to the door, and, as it closes, she stands against it for a moment. There is a silence.* HESTER *is slowly unravelling her knitting but is unaware of it. The black wool falls in spirals about her chair.)*

HESTER *(suddenly):* It's an old house. I was born here. *(Then in a strange, calm voice that seems to come from a long distance.)* You shouldn't let Bruce be so much alone. You lose him that way. He comes back to *us* then. He'll see you don't belong here unless you keep your hands on him all the time. (RUTH *looks curiously at* HESTER *but does not give her all her attention.* HESTER *suddenly becomes harsh.)* This is my house. You can't change it. (RUTH *starts to say something but remains silent.)* Father gave it to me. There isn't any room for you. *(In a high, childlike tone, like the sound of a violin string breaking.)* No room. *(She shakes her head gravely.)*

RUTH *(aware that something is wrong):* Hester —

HESTER *(as if she were telling an often-recited story to a stranger):* I stayed home when mother died and kept house for my little brother and father. *(Her voice grows stronger.)* I was very beautiful, they said. My hair fell to my knees, and it was black as a furrow turned in spring. *(Proudly.)* I can have a husband any time I want, but my duty is here with father. You see how it is. I can't leave him.

(RUTH *goes quickly to* HESTER.*)*

RUTH *(with anxiety and gentleness):* Hester, what are you talking about?

HESTER That's father's chair. I'll put his Bible out. *(She starts from her chair.)*

RUTH *(preventing her):* Hester, your father's not here — not for six years. You speak of him as if you thought . . . Hester —

HESTER *(ignoring* RUTH *but remaining seated):* When I was a girl I always filled the lanterns after supper. Then I was ready for his coming.

RUTH *(in terror):* Hester, I didn't fill them! I didn't fill the lanterns! *(She runs to the kitchen door and takes up the remaining lantern.)*

HESTER *(calmly):* Father called me the wise virgin then.

RUTH Hester, Bruce took one! He thought I'd filled them. It will burn out and he'll be lost in the blizzard.

HESTER I always filled them.

RUTH *(setting the lantern on the table):* I've got to go out after Bruce. If he gets down to the coulee and the lantern goes out, he'll never find the way back. I'll have to hurry! Where's the coal oil?

(RUTH *goes to the kitchen and returns with a can of coal oil and a pair of galoshes.* HESTER *watches her closely. As* RUTH *comes in with the oil,* HESTER *slowly rises and goes to her.)*

HESTER I'll fill the lantern for you, Ruth.

RUTH *(trying to remove the top of the can):* I can't get the top off. My hands are shaking so.

HESTER (*taking the oil can from* RUTH*):* I'll fill it for you.

RUTH Please, Hester. While I get my things on! *(Giving* HESTER *the oil can,* RUTH *runs to the footstool and hurriedly puts on her galoshes.)* I'm afraid that lantern will last just long enough to get him out there. He'll be across the field before I even get outside. *(She runs up the stairs.)*

HESTER *(standing motionless, the oil can in her hand):* You're going now. That's right. I told you you should go.

(RUTH *disappears up the stairs.* HESTER *moves a step towards the lantern, taking off the top of the coal oil can. She hesitates and looks for a moment after* RUTH. *With the strange lucidity of madness, slow, deliberately, she places the top back again on the can and, moving behind the table, sets it on the floor without filling the lantern.* RUTH *hurries down the stairs excited and alarmed. She has on heavy clothes and is pulling on her gloves.)*

RUTH Is it ready? (HESTER *nods.*) Will you light it for me, Hester? Please.

(HESTER *lights the lantern.)*

RUTH I'll put the light at the window. *(She crosses with the small lamp and places it at the window.)* Hurry, Hester! *(With a sob.)* Oh, if only I can find him!

(HESTER *crosses to* RUTH *and gives her the lantern.*)

(RUTH *takes the lantern and goes out. A gust of wind carries the snow into the room and blows shut the door after her.* HESTER *goes to the window.)*

HESTER *(her voice is like an echo):* The snow lies deep on the summer fallow . . . The snow is a moving shroud . . . a winding sheet that the wind lifts and raises and lets fall again. *(Turning from the window.)* They've gone. They won't be back now. *(With an intense excitement,* HESTER *blows out the lamp at the window and pulls down the shades. Her eyes fall on the bowl of hyacinths in the corner. Slowly she goes to it, takes it up and, holding it away from her, carries it to the door. Opening the door, she sets the flowers outside. She closes the door and locks it. Her eyes blazing with excitement, she stands with her arms across the door as if shutting the world out. Then softly she moves to the door of her father's bedroom, unlocks it, and goes in, returning at once with a pair of men's bedroom slippers. Leaving the bedroom door open, she crosses to the sideboard, takes up the Bible and, going to her father's chair, places the slippers beside it. She speaks very softly.)* I put your slippers out. *(She draws the footstool up to the chair.)* Everything will be the same now, Father. I'll read the one you like. *(She reads with quiet contentment.)* "And the winds blew, and beat upon the house; and it fell not; for it was founded upon a rock."

The wind moans through the old house as —

THE CURTAIN FALLS

Cold Feet Cured

Eric Nicol

Well, here it is the middle of October, time to start thinking about how we're going to keep our feet warm in bed this winter.

Any night now we're going to jump into bed, cry "Hallelujah!" and jump right out again. It'll be cold in there. Especially at the bottom. The bottom of the bed is where the cold bunches up and waits for a pair of unsuspecting feet to blunder into the trap.

I have already received one foot-warming suggestion from a reader, Mr. F. W. Heppenstall, R.N., of Lynn Valley. Mr. Heppenstall writes: "You can sleep warm by breathing through a piece of rubber tubing placed amongst the feet."

Before passing this suggestion on to you I thought I had better try it myself. I regret to say that though the feet prospered I had disturbing dreams of trying to siphon Burrard Inlet into a bucket. If this sort of dream is an improvement over the ones you've been having you might care to give Mr. Heppenstall's footnote a whirl.

The hot-water bottle I don't like, owing to a traumatic experience I had with a hot-water bottle as a child. The hot-water bottle waited until I was asleep one night, then unscrewed its stopper, so that I woke up suddenly in a lake. Like stout Cortez, I was filled with a wild surmise, encountering this in-board Pacific. I have been leary of hot-water bottles since. If they can't burn you or drown you they will leave their cold clammy bodies where your feet will find them in the morning. I don't recommend them.

But a wife is a useful rig. Or a husband. People with cold feet usually marry people with warm backs. A lot of warm-backed people think they have won a mate by their intelligence or beauty, never knowing that their main attraction is that of being a warm object that won't leak. This is fitting and right, since the old adage "cold hand, warm heart" also applies to feet, and the parky-peddled type is usually very loving once you get its feet out of your stomach, so they tell me.

If you don't want to go that high, bed socks are a good idea. There seems to be some prejudice against bed socks, as being unmanly or something. We Canadians are afraid of bed socks because the house might catch fire and we'd run out into the street and people would see that we slept in Argyles, almost as bad as sleeping in sin. This is a pity, because putting on a pair of bed socks that have been toasted in front of the fire and then piling into bed is one of life's more luxurious experiences.

Bed socks are especially helpful if you are a kicky sleeper. If you kick the bed-clothes out from under the mattress, exposing the feet (or if you sleep in a short bed), bed socks can often make the difference between waking up with feet and waking up with a couple of frozen haddock.

Still another cure for cold dogs is a big fat cat. The procedure here is, about a half hour before retiring, to take the cat, warmed by the fire, and put him on the bottom of the bed. When you are ready to climb in, you remove the cat and slide your feet into the place the cat has warmed with his body. You may feel that this is rough on the cat. Don't waste your sympathy. If he is anything like our cat he will wait until you have dropped off to sleep, then jump back on your feet and keep you awake while he washes himself and plucks cat harp music out of the coverlet. Kicking at the cat usually dislodges the bedclothes and you're right back where you started. I don't know why I mentioned it.

You notice that I have ignored the thermostatic-bedroom, electric-blanket crowd who can get into bed and be sure of finding it warm, rain or shine. These people don't know the meaning of cold feet, sleep in twin beds and get divorced at a frightening rate. Their problem, like their wiring, is more complicated. Some other time, maybe.

Drought

Maurice Rookwood

Year after weary year I plowed the fields
And laboured oft from dawn to setting sun.
With disc and harrow worked the rich black loam
And gloried in the thought of work well done.

Using the moisture from the winter's snow
The young green shoots came pushing through the soil.
And all the world was green and fair, as though
God promised rich reward for all my toil.

The grain was green and sturdy, bearing promise
Through all those happy days of glowing spring,
Of golden fields and busy days of harvest,
Of thresher's hum when geese are on the wing.

But as through all those long hot summer days
The sun shone brightly with increasing heat,
The rich green lush of grain turned pale, then yellow.
— I walked along the fields with lagging feet.

Day after day through air with heat a-quiver
The sun blazed hotly from a cloudless sky.
The wind came moaning with a sibilant whisper
Of drifting dust and sand — "Your crop must die."

The stubbled grain has long since dried and shrivelled.
My soil is cracked and broken like the sod.
The summer-fallow, too, has scorched and sickened.
My heart cries out, "Send rain! Send rain, O God!"

The Tale of a Young Cree

Barry Broadfoot

Dad had farmed around Shaunavon but the drought drove him out and we went north. It was there we lost Mom. She had a bad cough in the winter of 1936 and it got worse and we drove her to hospital in the wagon, it was full of hay, and we piled every blanket we had around her. But those 12 miles to hospital killed her. When Dad lifted her out to carry her into the hospital her mouth was open and her eyes were open and I said, "Dad, it's too late." It was pneumonia and it was 30 below and it took five hours to go 12 miles over those tracks they called roads in northern Saskatchewan. We buried her in town and then went back and told the kids.

There were five others and Dad took over our schooling, which mother had done. But he couldn't figure out algebra and he said about grammar that we should just put it down the way it sounded right, and we could all read, so he taught us history. Western Canadian history. He'd grown up with it. I can remember, he'd do the chores during the day, going with the team for marsh hay, and I was the mother and at nights after our meal of moose and turnips and coffee — which was just roasted barley with no sugar — he'd tell us of the old days. The Selkirk Settlers, the Nor'Westers and what a tough bunch they were, and the Riel Rebellion and the building of the Canadian Pacific Railroad, these things and more, and he'd act it all out. He'd establish about eight characters or more, or however many there were, and then he'd go through it as a play. Voices. Dialogue. Moving around, and there were the six of us staring open-mouthed, and if someone had looked through our window he probably could never have figured what the Sam Hill was going on.

A story might go on for a week or more, with Dad leaping and whooping and hollering and skulking around the shack, acting Indian, soldier, settler, cowboy, every part. It was crazy!

The best I remember was Almighty Voice. He was a Cree up around Batoche about 1895 and he killed a Mountie and it took half an army to run him to earth. Dad took about five days to tell this story, and naturally we were all in sympathy with Almighty Voice. Just a youngster, and fighting for what he felt was justice. Yes, he killed several men but it was white man's stupidity that caused it all. I don't know where he learned it, or whether he just made it up, but Dad sang us the Cree Death Song, the one Spotted Calf did for her son, and we went to bed crying that night.

That is the way history should be taught, by people who know it and love their country. Not these dry phrases out of a textbook written by some old man. We may have been hungry a lot of the time, but I can look back on those years as being pretty good years. Thanks to Dad.

Please Help Me

Andreas Schroeder and Rudy Wiebe

Perdue, Sask., 1933

It is with a very humble heart I take the opportunity of writing this letter to . . . ask you if you will please send for the underware in the Eaton order (made out and enclosed in this letter). My husband will be 64 in Dec. and has nuritis very bad at times in his arms and shoulders. We have had very little crop for the last three years, not enough at all to pay taxes and live and this year crops around here (West of Saskatoon) are a complete failure. My husband is drawing wood on the wagon for 34 miles and had to draw hay too, for feed for horses, this winter. He has to take two days for a trip and sleep under the wagon sometimes. He is away for wood today and it is cold and windy . . . I have patched and darned his old underware for the last two years; but they are completely done now, if you cant do this I really dont know what to do. We have never asked for anything of anybody before, we seem to be shut out from the world altogether — we have no telephone Radio or newspaper. For this last couple of years we . . . could not afford to have them. We used to enjoy your speeches on the Radio also the Sunday church services, as we cant get out very much in winter. If I can only get this underware for my husband I can manage for myself in some way. He has to be out in the cold, where I can stay in the house. . . .

The Prime Minister's Secretary Replies

. . . While you can realize Mr. Bennett has been inundated with similar requests, nevertheless in view of the health of your husband I have forwarded to the T. Eaton Co. Limited, order for high grade, heavyweight Wolsey underwear. . . .

I trust you will treat this matter as strictly confidential. . . .

Fort Macleod, Alta. (A Lawyer), 1931

. . . How in the world I can make ends meet this Winter, pay the accounts and keep going I cannot see. Folks that owe me just cannot pay what they owe, or even small parts of it.

Is there any possibility of there being a chance for me to earn five hundred or a thousand dollars on some special work this winter? Would it be possible that the Honourable Minister of Agriculture might have a spot. . . .

I trust I do appreciate the terrific (and that adjective is not too strong) pressures everywhere on the departments and the Ministers and I think I will understand in any event, but if — if — possible I truly need a little help to keep matters within reasonable bounds. . . .

Edmonton (An Accountant)

. . . I have found it impossible to obtain permanent employment to support my family. I would ask you if there is not a way of my obtaining this appointment (Income Tax Auditor) and if not this appointment, some position for which my training fits me and with definite future prospects later on.

I regret to further trouble you, but my position is desperate. I have come to the end of my resources, my daughter lies dangerously ill in hospital with spinal meningitis, my wife has a nervous breakdown and my little son is getting no care. I must get an appointment. My last court of appeal is to you . . .

Wainwright, Alta. (A Teacher)

. . . If I cannot get a school perhaps I would have to ask relief — and the chance of getting a school is very small even though I have splendid reports.

Sovereign, Sask.

. . . I have walked miles trying to sell toilet articles to buy my children clothes this was last fall all my children clothes are completely worn the town kindly gave them one suit of overalls and shoes but boys has a wonderfully way of wearing and tearing things quickly so you see Sir when this chain letter came it surely looks like a ray from heaven if I should by chance have got this money I would have bought myself a house here at 3 hundred put the rest in the bank & lived at least 4 yrs by that time my 2 oldest boys would be able to get work they would of course be pretty young & miss some good schooling but it couldnt be helped . . . We could be happy contented who want to live & sleep like cattle they even have a stall while my children & hundred of others sleep 3 and 4 in a bed if some of the wealthy ones tried this way of living they would soon start something quicker than chainletters. . . .

Two Letters from Benton, Alta.

February 19, 1935

. . . I suppose I am silly to write this letter but I haven't anyone else to write to so am going to hope and pray that you will read this yourself and help me or us rather.

We are just one of many on relief and trying to keep our place without being starved out. Have a good 1/2 section not bad buildings and trying to get a start without any money and 5 children all small. Have been trying to send 3 to school and live on $10.00 a month relief for everything, medicine meat flour butter scribblers. Haven't had any milk for 3 months but will have 2 cows fresh in March some time. Am nursing a 10 months old baby and doing all the work cooking washing mending on bread and potatoes some days. This is our worst winter as my husband has had to be home to look after the outside chores. Other winters he always made some money as we lived in town and I could manage alone.

As so worried on account of the children as we never have any vegetables except potatoes and almost no fruit and baby hasn't any shoes have kept him in old socks instead but now he is getting so he creeps and pulls them off so often. I would like to get a couple of little pigs this spring I am sure we can make a go of this place as its good land and doesn't blow if we would just manage until fall. Just had 70 acres in last year and the dry spell just caught it right along with the grasshopper although we poisoned most of them there were hardly any left by fall. I can't hardly sleep for worrying about it.

My husband doesn't know I am writing this letter but I just dont know what to do for money the children come to me about everything its the women and children who suffer in these terrible times, men don't notice things. I suppose you think I am maybe making things out worse than they are but I am not. Please help me by lending me some money and I will send you my engagement ring and wedding ring as security. I know I could pay you next fall because I like this place and we have a good deal on it no interest for 10 years. I raised 50 chickens and 2 red hens last summer now we have nearly forty hens but they are not laying yet. If you could just lend me 50.00 even I would be the happiest woman in Alberta and you would be the best Premier of Canada because you would have been the means of saving a whole family guess I had better go to bed. My two rings cost over a $100.00 15 yrs ago but what good are they when the flour is nearly all done and there isn't much to eat in the house in the city I could pawn them but away out here I haven't been off the farm this winter. Will expect to hear from you hope to anyway I am sure you will never be sorry if you do help us. . . .

(R. B. Bennett sent $5.00 as a gift.)

March 18, 1935

. . . Received your letter also the five dollars and thank you very much for it. Got quite a thrill when my little boy came in with the letter. Was rather disappointed as I needed more than five so much and did not expect you to give it to me but lend it till fall. However it helped a lot as my baby boy will have shoes in time for his 1st birthday also a bottle of cod liver oil & some oranges. They will be his first shoes and I am surely glad as keeping him in socks was about driving me dippy. If it wasn't for having to look after the children I wouldn't have to ask any man for help. You can't imagine what it is like to have them wanting things and not able to make a nickel. Social Credit would surely be a great thing for the women of this dried out country. I guess you are pretty busy so I won't write anymore. . . .

Loam Lake, Sask.

. . . Can you possibly help us as we are down and out. My husband his in very poor health & cannot work to keep me &

my four children he his a Returned man, & sure did his bit in the great war from 1915 until 1919 & absolutely no good now, in fact no man will employ him, because he cannot do a days work for a days pay, & in this town they give no Relief. Our rent is overdue & are expected to be put on the Road. We have no *food* in fact I had to go to a neighbour house to beg something to eat & some shoes for the kiddies to wear. Sir if you can possibly help us to get Direct Relief or get us the War Allowance which I have tried for & they turned it down. Something will have to be done quickly as my husband is getting desperate because he knows his wife & kiddies are starving when there is plenty in the land. I am not a *bum* & hardly ever complain but this is terrible. We are Cons. & always have been, & the Liberals will not help us but in my case it should have nothing to do with politics. It is a case of *starve to death & be quiet*. But this living on hardly anything as gone to far & my kids need food, clothes or it will be I will have to bundle my kiddies up and freight it to Ottawa with them.

Tales of the Klondike

Laura B. Berton

There was no word for almost two months — then a flurry of excitement as the bishop, looking gaunt and worn, came in by sleigh from Fort Yukon. He had a harrowing story to tell, and over the months that followed it came out bit by bit.

The route between Fort McPherson and Dawson City is a long and dangerous one, and those stampeders who had attempted to reach the Klondike by this passage had been as long as two years on the trail from Edmonton. It was said that for every hundred men who started on this route only fifty succeeded in achieving their goal. Certainly more men died on the Rat River Divide than on all the other trails of '98 combined. But the bishop was used to the journey and made it almost every year. His route led him up the Peel River to the Rat and up the Rat to the end of navigation. Then he would portage over the mountain divide to the West Rat and down that river to the Porcupine, which, in turn, led to Fort Yukon on the river.

On this trip the bishop's Indian guide fell ill and the bishop and his companion, C. J. Johnston, another Church of England missionary, had to turn back. Partly because of this delay the freeze-up caught them before they crossed the divide. A blizzard sprang up and the river began to run with blocks of ice, so they were forced to abandon their canoe and strike out on hand-made snow-shoes improvised from willow boughs and moccasin strips. Then with three days' provision — all they had with them — they started mushing in the general direction of the divide. Before long they realized they were completely lost in a maze of mountains, deep crevasses and frozen rivers. Soon the thick fog of forty below descended on them, obliterating familiar landscapes and seeping with chill fingers through their light clothing. To their horror, after each day of heavy mushing, the two men would arrive back at the spot where they had abandoned the canoe. Their provisions were exhausted and they were down to a single spoonful of Grape Nuts each and whatever berries they could find clinging to the leafless, snow-covered cranberry bushes.

It was at this juncture that Bishop Stringer hit on an idea for which he was to become famous, and which was later to inspire a scene for Charlie Chaplin's motion picture *The Gold Rush*. For years he had heard of and seen the Indians boiling beaver-skins with the hair off and drinking the soup that formed. The bishop and Johnston decided to accomplish the same feat with their boots, which had walrus soles and sealskin tops. They scraped what hair they could from them and then, as the snow fell about them, built a fire and boiled the boots for seven hours, afterwards baking them on hot stones. They ate the result, which the bishop told me was tough and stringy, but palatable and fairly satisfying. Thus nourished, they again set out, but still got nowhere. Finally they decided to construct a platform and climb up on it to escape marauding wolves, who might have torn them to pieces as they waited for death. No sooner was this decision advanced than the bishop rejected it.

"I decided," he explained, "that if we were strong enough to build ourselves a platform to die on, then we might as well keep on living."

They trudged on through the snow until finally they reached a large river which neither recognized. The bishop broke the ice to see which way the current was flowing. It was going north, so he was sure he was on the Peel. This was heartening — and so was the marten trap they stumbled on under the snow, the first sign of humanity in more than a month. They ate the rest of their boots and stumbled on following the line of the river. Then in the distance they heard the sound of dogs and children and knew they were saved.

They were so exhausted it took them five hours to travel the final mile to the encampment. The bishop had lost fifty pounds and the Indians did not recognize him until he called one of them by name and muttered the single word "*iziquilsiz*", meaning "hungry". Neither man could walk any further, and the Indians who came out from the village to meet them had to carry them in on their backs.

The bishop told me that at first he found it very difficult to eat, and that even after he was able to take some meat, he found himself saving the bones and sneaking them into his pockets as a sort of reflex action acquired during those days when every morsel of seal-skin counted. When the two were strong enough to walk again they mushed back to Fort McPherson, where they regained their strength. This done, the bishop turned back again and walked the entire distance over the Rat River Divide in the dead of winter to Fort Yukon, where a sleigh brought him to Dawson. From this point on he was known as The Bishop Who Ate His Boots.

A month later, in January, there was a second flurry. We were playing bridge one evening, four of us, when Edmund Ironsides, the customs collector, called in. He had been up at St. Mary's Hospital visiting a friend when Jim Christie, who had fought a grizzly bear to a standstill the previous fall, had arrived, badly injured, but under his own power. He had been terribly mauled. I can still remember meeting Dr. Alfred Thompson later on that week, shaking his head and saying, "I really don't know how the man hangs on!"

Christie's story was as memorable as the bishop's, and it is still told in the Yukon as the greatest bear story known. The battle occurred on a cold, snowy day in late October as Christie, a wiry, grizzled man, was following the trail of a giant bear that had robbed his cache of moosemeat. He was climbing the river bank when he looked up and saw an enormous grizzly charging at him from a distance of thirty feet. Without turning a hair Christie unslung his Ross rifle and shot the bear full in the chest. The bear kept coming. At four feet Christie shot him point blank in the face. The bear still didn't stop. A moment later he had dashed the rifle from the trapper's hand, forced Christie's head into his mouth and commenced to crush it.

Christie continued to fight back. He pushed his right arm between the bear's jaws and dragged his head free. The bear sank his teeth through Christie's wrist, smashing the bones like egg-shells. The two of them began to roll over in the snow, the bear with his teeth now sunk in Christie's thigh, each hugging the other in a death grip, the blood of each pouring over the body of the other. Then the bear suddenly relaxed its grip and rolled over dead.

Christie was in terrible shape. His scalp was torn down over his eyes and his skull bones punctured. One eye was blinded. Both jawbones were broken and one dislocated. His lips and cheeks were gashed, his wrist broken, and his jaw hung down against his chest. He staggered to his feet, struggled out of his jacket, wrapped it around his torn skull, then twisted the sleeves to support his broken jaws. His cabin was six miles away but he was pretty sure that his partner, George Crisfield, would call in at a deserted cabin a mile distant. He headed there first, and using the bullet end of a cartridge wrote this blood-smeared note on a board of the table:

Dear George — I am all in, but will try to reach camp. Will keep to the river. You will find a dead grizzly near our cache. Good-bye! Jim.

Christie realized that the narrow valley of the newly frozen Rouge River, uncertain though it was, was still the best trail to his cabin. He struggled along for hours, tormented by pain and slightly delirious. During the final mile, almost blind, and staggering like a drunken man, he began to suffer terrible cramps in his legs and had to stop periodically to massage them. Half a mile from the camp he found himself caught in a canyon with open water, quite impassable, straight ahead. He now had to struggle up the rocky bluff, slipping and falling in his own blood and undergoing what he later described as "a struggle I would not endure again for nine lives." Finally he reached his destination, built a fire, and tried to force a cup of whisky through his broken jaws. The only way he could manage this was to mix the whisky with cold tea, pour it into a shallow basin and then place his face into the basin and swallow. This done he rolled on to his bed of spruce boughs and lay there in agony waiting for his partner.

He waited five hours. When George Crisfield arrived, Christie found he could not speak properly because of his broken jaw, and in the gloom Crisfield took him for an Indian. Christie made him understand that before lighting the lamp and looking at him he was to take a stimulant. Crisfield, wondering, did so. Then he lit a lamp, pulled the robe from Christie's head, and staggered back crying, "Oh, my God, Jim!" over and over again.

Crisfield, shaken at first, recovered and began to search

about for ways and means to move Christie to the nearest trading post, at Lansing on the Stewart River, fifty miles away. He and some Indians finally rigged a toboggan into a movable stretcher and set out with Christie strapped on to it. But the Indians were loath to move a dying man and had to be bribed heavily to go at all. The jerking of the dog-team over the mountain passes kept Christie in constant pain and his morale was not bolstered by the Indians, who had a habit of leaning over him and whispering, "Are you dead yet, Jim?" It was a four-day journey to Lansing and after the party arrived Christie's clothes had to be cut from him. For two months he hovered between life and death, unable to take any nourishment at all except soup, because his broken jaws had set in such a way that his teeth could not meet. Then with two other men he set out on New Year's Day with toboggans and snowshoes for Dawson. Despite his injuries, Christie spent as much time on snow-shoes, breaking trail, as he did on the toboggan. Seventeen days later he arrived in Dawson. The doctors looked at him and shook their heads. A week later he was sent Outside on the Overland Stage. (Another man on the stage was Bishop Stringer, who had himself just come through his own ordeal.) Christie underwent a series of operations over a six-month period which in the end mended his bones as well as his strength. Indeed, when the Great War came five years later, Christie was one of its heroes. He won a Distinguished Conduct Medal, a commission in the field, a Mentioned in Dispatches and a Military Cross. I visited him decades later when he was well on in life, a white, agile little man, living quietly with his wife on Salt Spring Island on the British Columbia coast, with only a slight scar visible on his scalp as evidence of that terrible winter when — while the rest of us were dancing in the A. B. Hall — he fought for his life after his famous battle with a grizzly.

Courage, Canoes, and Whales

Douglas Leechman

Though it had been light for an hour or so now, it was impossible to see more than a canoe length from the cedar dugout in which eight men sat and shivered as they waited for the sun to rise high and dispel the fog. The slow heaving ground swell which never leaves the Pacific seemed like a conscious effort of the water to struggle free from the oppressive weight of the thick white mist pressing upon it so heavily.

Gradually one quarter grew distinctly lighter and a cool breeze, scarcely perceptible, stirred the fog into involuntary, reluctant movement. The breeze came, they knew, from the landward. An hour later the fog lifted and the vague mass of mountains far to the east, land clouds banked above them, told where lay their Vancouver Island home.

The day before they had been dragged far out to sea by a wounded and furious whale, only to have him pull free at last from their harpoon, when he felt the sting of what they had hoped would prove his death blow. For five long hours they had struggled with him. The first harpoon had been well and deeply planted; the floats, made from the hides of seals inflated with air, had been tied on to the twisted spruce root ropes, until no less than the traditional fourteen of them impeded the monster in his efforts to sound.

Again and again the Nootka Indians had paddled furiously after him, keeping a sharp look-out for the last tell-tale little float, made from a seal's stomach, which always rose to the surface long before the whale re-appeared after sounding. Each time they had calculated to a nicety where he should come to the surface, but he had always seen them, spouted vigorously, drawn a huge breath of fresh air, and sounded once again, before they could get close enough to plant a second harpoon in a vital spot.

At last their chance had come. Everything depended now on one skilful plunge of the harpoon. Balanced easily with his left foot on the little platform wedged in the bow of the canoe, taking careful aim at the right spot in the broad back, between the blow-hole and the dorsal fin, the harpooner had delivered what should have been the fatal stroke. A slight roll of the canoe, the drifting of a brown kelp leaf over the whale's back, and the stroke had failed. Instead of reaching deep into the lungs, the harpoon had merely spurred the whale to one last desperate effort. To the disgust of the crew, the whale sounded, but the floats remained bobbing quietly on the patch of smooth and swirling water where their prize had rested but a moment before.

Silently the leader pulled in the lanyard of braided whale sinew and examined it. One of the two barbs of the harpoon had evidently remained, with the mussel-shell blade, in the wound; the other barb, cracked almost in half, dangled by a twisting thread of sinew from the lanyard. One or two little feathers, thrust into the harpoon socket for good luck, clung wetly to the bone barb.

"The Chief of the Whales must be angry with us," said their leader. "Is there one among us who has not bathed as he should have done, or who has not sung the songs that should be sung?"

No one answered. Indeed, most of the men still bore on their sides the scratches of the bundles of four hemlock twigs with which each had four times scrubbed himself till he bled, such was their sincerity in performing their ceremonial ablutions.

Then night had fallen and, with the night, the choking fog. There was serious risk of finding themselves paddling still farther out to sea, instead of towards home, if they kept on while the mist blotted out the guiding stars and the long dark loom of the coast range.

With a light cedar-bark line, they moored their dugout to half a dozen kelp stems, floating there on the surface, but firmly anchored by their holdfasts to the rock-strewn bottom, many feet below. There the Indian whale hunters had ridden out the night, huddled for warmth in their cloaks of finely shredded cedar bark. It was an old seaman's trick, known to their ancestors, and still used by their descendants.

Now that morning had come and landmarks could be seen again, they slipped the line from the friendly kelp and started for home. No songs of jubilation and success, not much talking, no laughter.

While still ten miles from shore, a sleeping whale rolling on the quiet surface of the water lay not a bow shot from their course. Silently the sharp cut-water of the canoe parted the waves and, as silently, the skilfully shaped paddles, pointed and formed with the experience derived from generations of half-conscious experiments, sped them towards their quarry. The sleeping whale neither saw nor heard the coming canoe, which was brought to a stop just a paddle-length to the left of him as he wallowed in the trough of the ground swell.

Poised, with the heavy shaft of yew wood uplifted in both hands, the harpooner waited till the whale's back was waist deep below the water, so that no vicious flirt of the giant tail would have a chance to strike and split the canoe. When everything seemed favourable, the man next to the harpooner in skill and experience, whispered, as was his right, "Now!"

Leaping clear of the canoe, all his weight and will behind it, the leader drove the harpoon deep into the broad, round back. Immediately there was a violent swirl of water, the vast head rose high above the canoe, higher and higher till it seemed that the beast must fall right on them. Then, incredibly slowly, it arched over in a long graceful curve, and the whale plunged deep into the safe and sheltering ocean. Rapidly the men got the long coils of line running freely and bent on the seal-skin floats as the line went overboard.

Five minutes later the whale rose and spouted. Not vapour alone, but vapour deeply stained with blood. A great shout went up from the canoe, for they knew by this crimson sign that he was mortally wounded. Then minutes later, the end had come.

One of the younger men slipped easily overboard and cut a hole in the whale's lower lip through which he passed a tough line of braided elk-hide. Carrying the line through another hole cut opposite in the upper jaw, he handed it back to the waiting men in the canoe. With the great mouth shut by the elk-hide line, the whale was prevented from swallowing quantities of water which would have made the huge body heavier and more unwieldy than ever.

Now the long slow task of towing their quarry back to the village was before them. Once their natural jubilation was over, there were no jokes or hearty laughter. Such conduct would not be pleasing to the Chief of All Whales. No songs but decorous ceremonial songs might be sung, no trivial topics should be discussed.

As they neared the beach, they could see the rest of the villagers awaiting them; the women were dancing ceremoniously. All during the absence of the hunters they had stayed quietly in their houses lest they should, by inadvertence, do something that should react unfavourably, in the magical sense, on their success.

Now they danced the dance of welcome to the whale, and the young men sang praises of his size, his wisdom, his beauty, his strength, and his generosity in visiting their humble village. Great clouds of drifting eagle down, the symbol of peace and rejoicing, were flung into the air as eager hands dragged the carcass as high up the beach as possible and they all settled down to the tiring business of cutting off the blubber and meat, rendering down the heavy slippery lumps into the thick rich grease which would garnish many a meal and serve as valuable barter with other tribes in the interior, those poor and contemptible people who lacked the courage and the skill to hunt and kill the mighty whale from an open canoe, many weary miles from land.

Eskimo Whalery at Tuktoyaktuk

Nancy Davis

As Tolik (''Bird''), the 28-foot gasoline-engine powered whale-boat rounded the gravelly point of the island and entered the sheltered bay, the tail and flipper of a whale lashed to the side of the boat showed white above the water. Tolik came in close to the sloping, pebbly beach: the whale was cut loose from the side and made fast with a rope around his tail to a big rock in the cove. Here, on the shore, a few driftwood posts with crosspieces constituted the racks for the ''whalery''.

Whaling is the chief summer occupation of the native population of the island of Tuktoyaktuk on the coast of the Western Arctic. During the short summer the Eskimos accumulate some of their food supply for the winter months.

We hastened down to the whalery. A number of Eskimos sat or stood around watching the proceedings with good-natured interest. A few — families of the hunters, apparently — aided in the cutting up.

The whale lay ten or twelve feet out from the shore, and a couple of little boys were throwing stones at the white, rubbery-looking bulk. It was perhaps fourteen feet long, pure creamy-white in colour, a shapeless-looking creature that might, by its appearance, have been moulded out of plastic or soap. Its blunt, comical snout, and little piggy eyes gave it a mild, foolish expression.

These white whales, we were told, are really not whales at all, but a kind of porpoise found in great numbers in Arctic waters. Sometimes they are found in great schools that extend for miles, white backs flashing on every side as the animals rise to the surface. In such a school, many are cow whales with little calves. The latter, in contrast to the adults, are greyish in colour, and rise and submerge in perfect unison with their mothers' timing.

Several men now laid hold of the line that tied the whale to the rock, and hauled the animal in until they could work in water that was no more than ankle deep. Then three of them commenced to cut it up, working with the speed and precision of experienced butchers, their long-bladed knives flashing in the sunlight.

The head and tail were removed first and the water all about the body of the whale rapidly reddened.

We stood a short distance from the scene of operations, endeavouring to work around to the windward side of the whalery. But the whole area, wind or no wind, was pervaded with the stench of dead and gone whales, of drying and decaying fish, with odours appalling and hitherto unknown. One of our number was blessed with a bad cold: we envied her her immunity to smells.

A couple of women joined the men at the cutting up. Each one carried her *ulu,* a crescent-bladed knife with handle at the top of the crescent. In an incredibly short time, they had a rectangle of skin and blubber, about six feet by six, floating in the shallow water. The blubber below the skin was three or four inches in thickness; the women had separated it so perfectly from the purplish-black flesh underneath it that only here and there did a dark streak show where a shred of muscle still clung to the creamy fat.

Smaller pieces of skin and blubber were removed: the men proceeded to joint the carcass, and big lumps of purplish-black meat were laid upon the gravel. Above the workers, along the bank, the ever-hungry husky dogs, chained to their stakes, snarled and howled, scenting the fresh meat and unable to get at it. Momentarily, the gory mass of meat and bone shrank as it was cut down. The audience melted away, some of them carrying chunks of whalemeat.

Inside half-an-hour from the time the cutting-up began, nothing remained on the beach but the head and tail of the white whale, and the big piece of blubber and skin, from which the sea water, receding as the tide ebbed, washed all traces of blood.

A white whale, it seems, must be cut up as soon as the hunters bring it in. Otherwise, the action of the sun upon the carcass renders the blubber actively poisonous.

The next day we strolled down along by the whalery again. Nothing remained on the beach at all. Tolik was tied up further down the shore; the dogs complained fretfully of their hard lot and looked as starved as usual. But outside a tent set well back from the shore there was a good deal of activity.

Upon the usual rack, made from cross-pieces fastened to driftwood poles, many ragged slices of whalemeat hung. Cut quite thin (a quarter to half-an-inch in thickness), the dark meat was drying in the sun and the sea air for part of the family's winter food supply. Side by side with the meat dangled pieces of whale-hide from which most of the fat had been carefully scraped. This leather, creamy-white, quite water-proof and very light in weight, is extremely durable and makes fine soles for *mukluks* (Eskimo boots).

Close beside the rack, an open fire burned. Over it, a gasoline barrel, cut down and fitted with a wire handle, served as a kettle for boiling the blubber. Cut into rough pieces about six inches each way, with the skin still attached, it bubbled and steamed, giving off a heavy, oily odour. Occasionally the woman tending the fire and the pot stirred up the blubber with a fork wired onto a long stick. At intervals she cut out a few pieces and laid them to drain and dry upon a canvas spread out on the ground beside her.

Whale blubber so treated is less fatty and opaque in appearance than the raw fat, but still creamy in colour, still oppressively oily in odour. It is known as *muktuk,* and is a favourite Eskimo food. Frozen solid in the winter, *muktuk* rates with the Eskimo much as ice cream does with us, and has the added advantage of being both extremely nourishing and very rich in heat-producing calories. White men who have eaten it say that, in its frozen form, *muktuk* is not too oily, and has no objectionable flavour.

An odd-looking, bottle-shaped object, bright scarlet in colour, and tied up at either end like a balloon, caught our attention. It was the stomach of the white whale being dried in the sun on top of a gas barrel to make a container. This large membrane, inflated and tied thus, is over two feet long. In August, when the little tundra berries are ripe, a supply of them is picked and stored in such containers to add variety to an otherwise monotonous meat-and-fish diet.

We reflected that the Eskimo seemed to waste nothing: meat, bones, fat, hide, intestines of the white whale, all were utilized. Subsequent observation confirmed the fact. Outside a little house of weather-beaten driftwood logs, more whale-meat dried on a rough wooden rack; beside it stood a covered gas barrel. Curiously, we lifted the lid and peered in; quickly we replaced it and reeled away, greenish in the face. All the odours of the whalery were packed into the barrel, full of meat and fish scraps, with bits of yesterday's whale on the very top. The lean dogs howled protestingly, and we assumed that the barrel contained their rations.

As we passed the tiny Anglican mission church, Archdeacon Marsh stepped out the back door.

"Been visiting?" he enquired cheerfully.

We explained that we had been following up the fate of the white whale.

"Great stuff, muktuk and dried whale meat," he added enthusiastically. "Tastes good on a winter's day after several hours on the trail. Like to try it?"

He turned to an Eskimo woman standing nearby and spoke rapidly in Eskimo. A minute later a piece of dried whale meat was thrust into our hands. Black, coal-black it was, stringy in texture, so tough we could hardly break a bit off it. It might well have been a long string of semi-petrified tar, or a tangled, but still durable black leather shoelace.

"That's it!" said the Archdeacon, beaming. His helpers beamed too: they all wore a look of expectation. Although the whale-meat had next to no odour in that desiccated form, we couldn't rise to the occasion. We thanked the Archdeacon and his helpers, and said that we would put the whale meat among our souvenirs of the north. Since then, it has disappeared.

Although the food of the white man, in tins or packages, is quite easily available to these Eskimos of the Western Arctic, most of them seem to prefer their native diet. Many homes serve both kinds of food, but none seem to abandon entirely the native staples of fish, whale meat, and *muktuk*.

Season of Leaving (Sylvan Lake, Alberta)

Lorne Daniel

i

The season to leave is spring
or possibly fall
Summer holds
as it held my forefathers:
green and tangling
growing back
back where I cut it down
and trimmed its wildness
last year
Winter white challenges
with its assault on activity
of all kinds; snow traps
quickly, quietly
Even now the white weight
hugs the barn
towards the ground

ii
In town the buildings are all squat
half-sized and humorous
All winter long the windows
and skin-happy swimmers
have been in hiding
behind boards, terrorized
by the stark flat miles of wild ice
On the way, driving down to Sylvan
I can see shades of the Pacific
— dark, warm, and blue —
rolling over white-profiled mountains
Soon the seasonal decay begins
again, the snow turning brown
the winter an empire gone decadent and soft

iii
I have stopped
in the past, stayed
to add new limbs of life
to old wood
(always wood) frames:
new timbers, squared and strong
forced under the old
nailed into place as saviours
of some sad structure
Lately, though, I've been remembering
long-necked beer bottles
dark and musky
cob-webbed to roughed-in windowsills:
I wonder if the statement I make
will stand as long

iv

Years ago, David Thompson
axed his way through trees
near here, en route to
Rocky Mountain House and beyond
Now the Government of Canada
calls in engineers with fine instrumentation
to keep the last
remains of the fort
from washing down
the North Saskatchewan River
Nature keeps doing that:
washing back
downstream
down east
these pretences of civilization

In spring, I find myself
running with the water

FINISHING TOUCHES
James P. McLachlan
10 11 12 13 14 15 16 17 18 19 20 21

Invitation in September

Edwin Ash

Come with me!
Do not sit sighing here for summer
When lombardies like yellow candle flames
Light all the roadway to the river's edge;
When the sky is wind-washed,
Sparkling and blue,
And all along the fences
Twittering swallows gather musically
Like notes strung out upon a stave;
When asters prink the rippling roadside grass
With white and purple stars.
Come and rejoice with me
In Autumn's far flung tapestry —
Bright ochred golden rods whose threads weave
back and forth
Between rich reds and somber browns of fallen
leaves
And berries gleaming dusky blue.
Touch my hand lightly, friend, and follow me;
Now's not the time for sad contemplation.
We'll garner all September's plentitude
Before the winter weighs the scene
With new white blossoming.

Cricket Song

Myra Smith Stilborn

In the grass the homely cricket,
Like a clock we do not see,
Ticks away the sun-parched seconds
Of the summer, faithfully.

Dallying, we fail to notice
When the measured notes run down,
Till surprised we find the summer
All packed up and leaving town.

Appointed Time

Violet M. Copeland

"The geese fly south tonight," Grandmother said,
Settling the copper boiler on to heat
over the wood fire in the kitchen stove,
The best spot saved for the big porridge pot
beside the kettle, boiling lustily
for morning tea. Breakfast before the wash
could rub the ripples off the washboard's glass,
Then dishes; "unto everything a time."

"Tonight they'll go." Arms searching elbow-deep
in apron pockets, searching out the pins
among her clippings, balls of rolled-up string,
letters from home, the flower-seeds she's saved.
She squinted upwards where an egg-yolk sun
hung stiffly in the greyness. Poplar boughs
clutched her with hostile fingers as she passed,
hanging her white wash on the twisted wires,
pegging them firmly: wind brewed in that sky.

"Too soon for geese; the moon's not bound to change

for three more days, and then we'll have a storm,''
Grandfather said, and tapped a wary pipe
under her sharp eyes. Grandma said, ''You'll see.
The old owl hooted twice, last night, and twice
just breaking dawn. The geese fly south tonight.''

We finished up the wash, and dumped the tubs,
scrubbed floors, and started supper. Nothing stirred,
but just come sunset, had the sun stayed out
instead of sulking back behind a cloud,
we heard the honking. Spilling out the door,
we saw great vees spread high above our heads
Black-winged against the sky, and heading south,
Patterned with boldness on the evening sky.
Caught by an instinct ancient as their own.
Grandmother knew. The geese flew south tonight.

Wild Geese Passing

F. Elsie Lawrence

The geese have gone south, the geese have gone over;
High overhead I heard them crying,
Far and away I watched them flying.
Their strange wild cry made me start and shiver
Like something lost may be gone for ever.
Summer is dead, and autumn dying,
And the cold north wind at the windows sighing.

Oh, to have wings, to be strong and lonely!
What is our strength if our bonds are stronger;
We have a watch that we must be keeping.
Winter is like a foeman creeping
Close to the doors while the folks are sleeping.
The stars wax brighter, the nights grow longer,
And green lights out of the north are leaping.

The geese have gone over, the geese have gone by,
But we must stand fast for the winter's unfolding.
It is work for the hand, a long siege for the holding.
We dare not accept the far flight with its danger,
For the child in the crib, for the beast at the manger.
We are bred to the north; there is ice in our moulding,
But our hearts may go out to the cry of a stranger,
Though our souls must answer a wild bird's cry.

Skipping Rocks

Artella Davies

Skipping rocks
Across a dancing, rushing river
Trying to reach
All things in life
Before they are dammed off

But the hand grows old
Only three skips this time
Used to be nine
Or ten

The old man and the river
White foam is gathering
Along the water's edge

What Are the Best Years

Ray Bagley

What are the best years of one's life
When all is said and done,
Are they the years that have slipped away
Or those that are yet to come.

And who can say till the last one's here;
How can we agree
For the years that brought you the greatest joy
May not have been good to me.

What of the trails we journeyed o'er,
What of the plans we made,
I sometimes wonder if the things I did
Were the price I paid.
Still I'm eager to know what lies yonderly
Or down in the Valley's cup
And I reckon I'll ride a few more trails
'Ere I hang my saddle up.

At eventide beneath the pines
By campfire's ruddy glow
I like to sit and toast my shins
And think of folks I know.
Friends like you of bygone days
Wherever you may be
I'd dearly love to Share the Wealth
The wealth of memory.

Prospector

Patrick Lane

Old man, you prospected summer
country of caves and gold.
With the rattlesnake and the spider
you were a black widow without a mate
gone deep chrome yellow —
you shared with the sun
a babble of flowers and full
brown flawless centres where
you walked in a wilderness
of golden sleep.

Once I was a child
and saw you touch a mountain
wasp with your finger
tip to wing he didn't move
but shivered gently his petal shells
of yellow and black in the wide corner
of August. You watched solitary
wasps float down sunflower fields.

Old man, I dreamed you
wandered the mountains
in spring and planted
the hills with golden flowers.
When they found you
they said you were dead
but I knew that the wasps
had planted their eggs in you
and flowers were growing
out of your sleeping eyes.

Good-bye

E. Pauline Johnson

Sounds of the seas grow fainter,
   Sounds of the sands have sped;
The sweep of gales,
The far white sails,
   Are silent, spent and dead.

Sounds of the days of summer
   Murmur and die away,
And distance hides
The long, low tides,
   As night shuts out the day.

Acknowledgements

The editor wishes to thank the authors and publishers for permission to include the following in this anthology.

Alpine Club of Canada for "A Trip to Mt. Edith Cavell" by H. E. Bulyea from the *Canadian Alpine Journal*.

R. Ross Annett for "Babe and the Bully" from the *Saturday Evening Post* (January 26, 1957).

Pierre Berton for "Tales of the Klondike" by Laura B. Berton.

Elizabeth Brewster for "Jamie" from *Passage of Summer*.

The Canadian Publishers, McClelland and Stewart Limited for "The Mysterious North" by Pierre Berton from *The Mysterious North*. For "The Frost" and for "Tunnel Mountain" by George Bowering from *Rocky Mountain Foot*. For "Lake Minnewanka" and for "Sunrise on Lake Louise" by Ella Elizabeth Clark from *Indian Legends of Canada*. For "Lightning Storm" by Sid Marty from *Headwaters*. For "Prairie Impression" by Margot Osborn from *Saskatchewan Harvest 1955*. For "A Field of Wheat" by S. Ross.

Sharleen M. Chevraux for "The Golden Time" from *Heritage*, (September/October 1973).

Clarke, Irwin & Company Limited for "Sunrise North" by Elizabeth Brewster from *Sunrise North* (1972).

Violet M. Copeland for "Appointed Time" from *Heritage*.

Copp Clark Limited for "Prairie at Evening" by Wilfred Eggleston. For "Wild Geese Passing" by F. Elsie Lawrence. Anyone knowing a current address for these authors is asked to contact the publisher at 517 Wellington Street West, Toronto, Ontario. M5V 1G1.

Marjorie Dingwall and Family for "The Prairies" from *The Alberta Golden Jubilee Anthology*.

Doubleday Canada Limited for "Mother Saved the Homestead" and for "We Didn't Know What a Mosquito Was" by Barry Broadfoot from *The Pioneer Years 1895-1914*. For "The Tale of a Young Cree" by Barry Broadfoot from *Ten Lost Years*.

Betty Dyck for "Telephone Poles" from *Spirit of Canada*.

Gage Educational Publishing Limited for "Harvest Time" by E. Pauline Johnson from *The Canadian Reading Book*. For "A Young Farmer" by James M. Moir from *Family Chronicle*. For "Cricket Song" and for "The Gopher" by Myra Smith Stilborn from *Rubaboo 3*, W. J. Gage Ltd. (1964). For "The Alberta Homesteader" from *Canada's Story in Song*, W. J. Gage Ltd. (1965).

Marci Gamble for ''Prairie Season''.
A. Leonard Grove for ''Snow'' by Frederick Philip Grove.
Hancock House Publishers Ltd. for ''And My Heart Soars'' by Chief Dan George from *My Heart Soars*.
Hodder & Stoughton Canada Limited for ''At Crow's Nest Pass'' and for ''Good-bye'' by E. Pauline Johnson from *Flint and Feather*.
Bruce Hutchison for ''The Men in Sheepskin Coats'' from *Unknown Country*.
Patrick Lane for ''Pacific Edge'' and ''Prospector''.
Douglas Leechman for ''Courage, Canoes, and Whales'' from *Indian Summer*.
Macmillan Company of Canada Ltd. for ''Carrion Spring'' by Wallace Stegner from *Wolf Willow*. For ''Please Help Me'' by Andreas Schroeder and Rudy Wiebe from *Stories from Pacific and Arctic Canada*.
Miriam Mandel for ''My Prairies''.
Mrs. Margaret McCourt for ''Alberta'' and for ''Saskatchewan'' by Edward A. McCourt from *The Road Across Canada*.
Jody McCurdy for ''The Wild''.
Anne Marriott McLellan for ''The Wind Our Enemy'' by Anne Marriott from *Horizon*.
James M. Moir for ''Where He Guides the Tractor'' from *The Alberta Poetry Yearbook 1972* and for ''Berry-Picking'' from *Heritage* (July/August 1977).
New Leaf Publications Ltd. for ''The Wheat-Land'' by Mary Weekes from *Saturday Night* (April 8, 1933).
Eric Nicol for ''Cold Feet Cured'' from *Twice Over Lightly*.
Olive Nugent for ''City Heat Wave'' from the *Alberta Poetry Yearbook 1965*.
Peter Whyte Foundation (Archives of the Canadian Rockies) for ''What Are the Best Years'' by Ray Bagley.
Laura Rashley for ''Prairie Gold'' by R. E. Rashley from *Saskatchewan Harvest 1955*.
Samuel French Ltd. for ''Still Stands the House'' by Gwen Pharis Ringwood.
Barbara Sapergia for ''Haying Time, 1953'' from *Number One Northern*.
Saskatchewan Archives Board for ''A Winter in the Lost Horse Hills'' by R. L. Gibson and for ''Lizards, Lizards, Lizards'' by Robert Martin, both from *Saskatchewan History*.
Peter Stevens for ''Prairie'' from *A Few Myths*.

Andres Suknaski for ''Lanterns'' from *Leaving,* Repository Press.
Talon Books Ltd. for ''A Mountain Journey'' by Howard O'Hagan from *The Woman Who Got On at Jasper Station & Other Stories* (1977).
Thistledown Press Ltd. for ''The Hotel in Ituna'' by Glen Sorestad from *Prairie Pub Poems.*
University of Alberta, Community Relations for ''Eskimo Whalery at Tuktoyaktuk'' by Nancy Davis from *The New Trail.*

While every effort has been made to trace the owners of copyrighted material and to make due acknowledgement, we regret having been unsuccessful with the following selections:

''Invitation in September'' by Edwin Ash
''Moraine Lake'' by R. H. Blackburn
''Season of Leaving (Sylvan Lake, Alberta)'' by Lorne Daniel
''Skipping Rocks'' by Artella Davis
''This Valley'' by Myrna Harvey
''The Promise'' by Bob Mason
''Field in the Wind'' by Floris McLaren
''Autumn'' by Margot Osborn
''Drought'' by Maurice Rookwood
''An Old-Timer Remembers'' by ''Seventy''
''Kitsalano'' by Alexander M. Stephen
''Gibsons is Gone'' by Ken Sudhues
''Hailstones and Character'' by Ken Wotherspoon